Y0-AQV-447

THE PROSE AND POETRY SERIES

Across the

Blue
Bridge

SECOND EDITION

FLOY WINKS DeLANCEY
Associate Professor of English,
New York State University Teachers College,
Brockport, New York

WILLIAM J. IVERSON
Professor of Education
and Specialist in Reading,
Stanford University

Illustrations by Guy Brown Wiser Associates
Design by Stefan Salter

THE L. W. SINGER COMPANY
A Division of Random House, Inc.

| Syracuse | Atlanta | Chicago | Dallas | Menlo Park |
| New York | Georgia | Illinois | Texas | California |

© Copyright 1965, 1960 by The L. W. Singer Company, Inc.
All rights reserved under International and Pan-American
Copyright Conventions.
Manufactured in the United States of America 394-00081-1

CONTENTS

Unit One

ANIMALS WE KNOW

Unit Two

OUT OUR WAY

Unit Five

HISTORY MAKERS

Unit Six

FARAWAY TIMES AND PLACES

Unit Seven

HERO TALES

Unit Eight

A LONG STORY

UNIT ONE
Animals We Know

DUST OF SNOW

The way a crow
Shook down on me
The dust of snow
From a hemlock tree

Has given my heart
A change of mood
And saved some part
Of a day I had rued.

Robert Frost

"Dust of Snow" from *You Come Too* by Robert Frost. Copyright 1923 by Holt, Rinehart and Winston, Inc. Copyright renewed 1951 by Robert Frost. Reprinted by Permission of Holt, Rinehart and Winston, Inc.

BOONE McBRIDE'S
BURRO

Berta and Elmer Hader

Boone McBride whistled merrily as he led his new burro back to camp. His luck must be changing. To have found such a fine young animal was good fortune indeed.

The next day the little wild burro carried a prospector's kit on her back. The pack was not heavy, and she liked to be always on the move. She watched her master curiously as he chipped bits of rock off the ledges, while they wandered over the rugged mountain sides. Boone McBride was kind and gentle, and she trusted him. Though she balked at leading the way across some of the streams they came to, her master never lost his temper.

Day after day they plodded northward. Sometimes the trail was overgrown and McBride led the way. Sometimes the burro pushed on ahead, stopping from time to time to look around and see that her master was following. Days and weeks passed happily.

One day the trail they were following cut across some deep wagon ruts. McBride stopped. He had not seen anyone for weeks and knew that a rancher named O'Shea had taken up a homestead here some years before. He

"Boone McBride's Burro" from *Midget and Bridget* by Berta and Elmer Hader. Reprinted by permission of the authors.

and his wife and two children were the only people in the valley. Their nearest neighbor was forty miles away. It was two years since Boone had seen the O'Sheas and he knew he would be welcome.

Boone turned from the trail and followed the wagon tracks. The ranch house stood in a small clearing. Its unpainted wood was now a weather-beaten gray.

A dog barked as they drew near the house. A little girl about six years old stood on the porch and stared in amazement at Boone McBride and his burro, then in a wink she disappeared into the house. Before Boone had come much nearer, Brian O'Shea and his wife stood in the doorway with wide, welcoming smiles. The little girl peeked shyly from behind her mother's dress. The dog looked at the visitors suspiciously, but he stopped barking and his tail almost wagged. The burro kept an eye on the dog.

"Sure and it's me that said only this morning, Mary, it's high time Boone McBride came this way. And here you are. And have you found that rich mine and— But come in, man, and rest your weary bones. Here am I asking a lot of fool questions of you." O'Shea stopped talking and helped untie the knots in the pack rope.

Boone took his pack from the back of the patient burro and turned her loose in the corral back of the house. But as soon as he left her she went into the barn to see what she could find.

Boone returned to the house to answer the many questions he knew would be asked. The O'Sheas lived so far away that they seldom had a visitor. Mrs. O'Shea, fresh and pretty, seemed just a girl. It was hard for her to be living so far from people. Their home was humble, their comforts few, but what they had they gladly shared. Boone told them all the friendly gossip he had picked up along his path.

The little girl, too, had a question and piped up in her tiny voice, "What's his name?"

"That is Mr. McBride, honey," answered her mother.

"I . . . I meant the little horsey's name," said the child.

"That little horsey is a burro," chuckled McBride. "Well . . . well now, that reminds me. I have never given her a name yet. Let me think. What shall I call her? I have had many burros. There was Chiquita and Pancho and Carlos and Sacramento and Bolivar." Boone counted them one by one on his fingers. "What would you name her?"

The little girl hung her head. "I don't know many names. Do you think she would like Bridget? That's my name."

"Splendid. It's a grand name and I'm sure she will be proud to have it. Bridget the burro shall be. Bring a pail of water and we'll christen her this minute."

In great glee the child fetched a pail of water and went with Boone to the barn. She sprinkled a few drops of water on the surprised little burro's nose while Boone said,

"It's Bridget from now on you are. I hope you never bring disgrace on the fair name of Bridget. Here's a nice cool drink for you." Boone put the pail on the ground.

The burro drank the water gratefully. She looked at Boone and she looked at the little girl. Bridget was a nice name. Boone tied her in the corner stall.

When they returned to the house, little Danny O'Shea had given up chasing butterflies and grasshoppers because he was hungry and it must be nearly time for lunch. His sun-tanned face and sun-bleached hair showed very plainly that he spent as much time as possible out of doors.

"Hello, Mr. McBride," he said cheerily. "When did you come? I didn't see you." Danny was nine years old and remembered Boone's last visit with pleasure. He had been made rich then by a fine top and a bag of marbles, and now he could not help glancing at the pack lying on the porch.

"Can I help you in with the pack?" he asked Boone.

"Well, it is a pretty heavy pack for one man to manage all alone," said Boone. "Give me a hand, Danny, and we'll get it inside."

Danny felt very helpful as he picked up one end of the roll. It did not seem so heavy to him.

Bridget soon slipped outside again to see her namesake. She liked animals but was a little afraid of Tom and Ben, the work horses, because they were so big. Bess, the cow, was gentle as could be, but she looked very dangerous

when she shook her horns or stretched her neck and mooed loudly. Bridget liked the burro because she was so small and looked so gentle. But as she entered the barn she heard a loud "hee-haw" which so startled her that she dropped the handful of grass she had gathered for the burro and ran back to the house.

"Bridget's making awful noises, Mr. McBride," she gasped.

Boone smiled. "I thought I heard her calling me," he said.

Boone and the children went to the barn. The burro brayed again.

"Burros know what is good for them," said Boone. "She wants to be out of doors as long as there is any sun." He untied the halter and led the burro outside, turning her loose in the small inclosed field with Bess, the cow.

"Animals are like people," said Boone. "They get lonesome with no one to talk to.

"If I didn't have my little burro I would get very lonesome, too," said Boone. "Sometimes I don't have anyone else to talk to for weeks at a time."

"Gee," said Danny. "I never knew burros could talk. Daddy always said they were stupid."

"Stupid!" exclaimed Boone. "Why, many of those little animals are smarter than their owners and better prospectors, too. Why, I know a burro that found a rich mine for his owner."

"Gosh, Mr. McBride! Do you think your burro will find you a mountain of gold?"

"Maybe," said Boone. "I wouldn't be at all surprised if she did."

Boone stayed a week with the O'Sheas. Before leaving he unwrapped some mysterious parcels he had been carrying. Tobacco for his host and a bottle of perfume for Mrs. O'Shea. He opened a box and drew out a lovely little doll for rosy-cheeked Bridget. He handed Danny a box of water colors and a pad of drawing paper.

"I noticed that you liked to make pictures the last time I was here," he said.

Stammering their thanks, the children ran outside to examine their gifts.

It was with real regret that the rancher and his wife watched Boone's broad shoulders disappear as he followed his little burro around the bend in the road.

Boone was much farther north than he liked to be when the cool days and chill nights of late October told him it was time he headed for the warm desert lands.

Slowly they made their way south. Boone stopped to see his friend, big John Carlson, a miner, who lived in the mountains the year round.

Big John was disappointed that Boone was not staying for the winter. He pointed to the calendar and warned Boone of the danger of getting caught by a blizzard in the mountains.

"Don't be crazy, man," he said. "The snow will come any day. My nearest neighbors to the south are the Moystons. We haven't heard from them in a long time, but I think they are still homesteading. They are a good sixty miles from here, and most of the way is high in the mountains."

Boone had made up his mind to winter on the desert,

and much against the pleadings of his friend, he started south. He knew the trail and if a snow flurry did come, what of it? It would only be a light fall, no doubt, and he would soon be out of it.

Bridget was sorry when Boone threw the pack saddle on her back, for Dynamite, Carlson's burro, was good company. But when she found she was headed for the desert she hurried along the trail.

Boone made camp the third night and thanked his lucky stars that one more day would find them at the Moystons'. Bridget stayed near the campfire eating the green grass contentedly.

Her soft muzzle in his face awakened him at dawn. The little burro seemed uneasy. She sensed danger. A great stillness hung over everything. Dark clouds filled the sky to the north. Boone knew the signs—a storm was coming, and a bad one. He had no time to lose. In a few minutes the pack was on Bridget's back and they hit the trail. Once

through the pass in the mountains they would be safe. The Moystons lived in a sheltered valley at the foot of the next ridge. They pushed onward. Upward they climbed. The sky grew blacker. Sometimes it was so dark in the woods it was hard to see the trail. Then it started to snow. The air became thicker and thicker with the falling snowflakes.

They could no longer see the trail, but Boone had been over it many times before and there were plenty of markers. He had blazed trees and chipped guiding signs on rocky ledges. They trudged onward and upward through the snow. Their only chance lay straight ahead. They must reach the pass. The snowstorm had become a blizzard. There was no turning back now.

"Now we are in for it and no mistake, old girl," said Boone aloud.

Bridget didn't like the snow blowing in her eyes and ears, but she plodded steadily along after her master. The wind howled and shrieked about them while snow piled up in high drifts.

Boone patted his little burro's drooping head. "I'll make it easier for you," he said, as he untied his pack from her back and placed it at the foot of a large hemlock.

Leading Bridget, Boone pushed on. The biting wind cut through his heavy garments and chilled him to the bone. He felt numb, but to stop now meant certain death. He staggered along, and Bridget struggled after him. They rounded a great scarred rock on the mountain side. The wind calmed down.

They were through the pass at last. Boone was exhausted. He stumbled and fell. He lay quiet in the soft snow. Bridget nudged him gently with her nose. Boone didn't move. Bridget bumped him harder, and Boone struggled to his feet. He grasped the burro's short

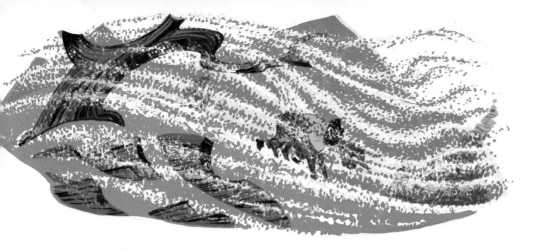

mane. He must depend on his little pal to find the way down the mountain.

Bridget, too, was tired from the long strain, but she pushed on. Boone somehow managed to get on the burro's back. His head fell forward, and he clasped his hands as tight as he could around the burro's short little neck.

Bridget moved slowly and carefully down the trail. Sure-footed though she was, there were times when she hesitated. A misstep would send her master and herself hurtling down the mountain side.

Slowly but steadily they descended the mountain. Down, down, always down. Through drift after drift she plunged with her precious burden. Bridget was tired, so very tired she felt she could not go much farther. Then she saw a glow of light through the gray mist of falling snow. She knew that where there was a light most likely there was a man, too. At last she came to the house. She heard voices. She threw back her head and uttered a feeble bray, and then she waited. Why didn't they come? She moved nearer the house and brayed again.

Jerry Moyston and his wife, Jill, stopped talking and looked at each other. Could it be possible that they heard the braying of a burro outside their door—faintly at first, then loud and hoarse?

"Sounds like a Rocky Mountain canary, Jill," said Jerry. "But what could he be doing outside in this sort of weather?" He opened the door and looked out.

Through the blinding storm he saw the little gray burro standing knee-deep in snow. And there was something that looked like a man on her back. Jerry could hardly believe his eyes. He dashed out into the snow and lifted the unconscious Boone McBride from the little burro's back. With his wife's help he got Boone into the ranch house. They put him on a couch in the corner.

"It's Boone McBride, Jill, and he's almost frozen to death. Make him a hot drink while I try and warm him up. I think he'll come out of it all right."

It was some time before Boone realized where he was. His first question was, "Where's Bridget, my burro?"

"I'll take care of her, now that you are all right," said Jerry. He put on his greatcoat and fur hat and went out. The burro was gone, but he followed the tracks in the snow. They led to the sheltered side of the house where the little burro stood close to the wall. Her head and her long ears drooped. She was exhausted.

"It's a medal you deserve for this deed, little burro," said Jerry. "I don't know how you ever found your way here." He patted her forehead encouragingly. "Come along. I'll put you in the barn out of the wind. You rest a while and I'll bring you a nice warm mash that will make you as good as new." Jerry led tired Bridget to the warm barn and put her in a stall next to Comanche, his pinto cow pony.

Bridget was too tired to lie down on the soft straw, but she closed her eyes. She hoped her master was all right now that she had found his friends. A little later Jerry returned with a pan of warm mash.

"Stow that away, ol' girl, and in the morning you will never know what a bad time you have been through." Jerry rubbed her nose gently and left the barn. The pinto pony looked at Bridget but asked no questions.

Bridget ate the warm mash. Then she lay down and slept.

The next day was bright and clear. The sun shone hotly down on the snow-covered hills. The countryside was white as far as you could see. The snow melted fast, and Jerry rode his pinto pony back over the trail and found Boone's pack.

Boone McBride was as good as ever after a few days' rest. As for Bridget, the one night's rest was all she needed and she was ready to start on the trail the next morning. A day or so later Boone thanked his friends and again took to the trail. He had enjoyed his stay with the Moystons, but he was anxious to get started, for he still had a long way to go.

When the heavy snows of winter blocked the roads and trails, Boone and Bridget were safely out of the snow country and slowly making their way across the sunny desert.

The next spring Boone McBride and his burro started across the desert earlier than usual. He counted on getting farther north than he had other years.

Some weeks later, as Boone stopped at the store of the rich La Plata Mine, a string of burros carrying ore passed by on their way to the railroad. Boone waved to the driver.

"Hello, Boone," said the storekeeper. "You and your burro are just in time. The burro boss is putting on another string and needs a driver."

Boone was in need of supplies and his money was low, so he was glad for the job. Counting Bridget, he had twelve burros in his string. Boone packed the heavy sacks of ore very carefully, for he knew from experience that a burro with a chafed back will not work. In his younger days his bad packing had rubbed some skin off his burro's back, and the next day she lay down on the ground when

he put the saddle on and wouldn't get up. He learned how to pack correctly from an old prospector, and he never had any trouble with his burros after that.

Sometimes Boone rode Bridget, but often enough he put a pack on her back and let her lead the string of burros. The ore was put on the cars at the railroad siding. After a short rest, Boone loaded the burros with provisions, coal, or timber to be taken back to the mines. Bridget got to know the trail so well she could almost go over it with closed eyes. No matter how hard the day's work had been, a good night's rest and plenty to eat found the burros fit for another hard day. Bridget enjoyed the company of the other burros at night, but Boone found the long evenings in camp quite dull. He began to feel restless and decided to hit the trail for the canyon country as soon as he was paid off.

One afternoon as he was making his return trip, Boone was startled out of his daydreaming by a sharp command to put up his hands. His eyes looked into the barrel of a gun, and he raised his hands above his head. A bandanna hid the lower part of the speaker's face, and Boone knew he meant to lead off the string of burros in order to get the company payroll which was in one of the boxes of provisions.

The bandit tied Boone to a big spruce, then turned and picked up the lead rope. "Come on," he growled.

Bridget did not like the stranger's voice. She knew that something was wrong. Still he might be one of the other

drivers, so she led the string after the bandit. When they came to the fork in the trail, he took the path away from the mine, but Bridget walked straight on leading the string. She knew the right direction. The bandit jerked on the rope. He swore at Bridget but could not make her turn around. He kicked her, but she became only more stubborn. Now she was sure there was something wrong.

"All right," growled the bandit, "I'll just turn you loose. Maybe these others are not so stupid." He cut Bridget loose from the string. Old Jerry followed the bandit. The rest of the string followed Jerry.

Bridget watched the burros disappear around the bend. Then she turned and trotted back along the trail.

The longer he stood there, tied, the angrier Boone got. He was so taken up by his own bitter thoughts he did not notice the little burro trotting along the trail, and she was almost upon him before he saw her.

"Bridget!" cried Boone in astonishment. Then he looked at her sternly.

"Listen to me, Bridget. It's many a knot you have untied

when I didn't want you to. Now be a good girl and untie those knots in back of me." Boone wiggled his hands and tried to reach the knots.

Whether Bridget sensed that the knots held Boone a prisoner or not, in a very short time her strong teeth had loosened them and Boone was free.

The bandit was so busy opening the boxes in his search for the payroll that he neither saw nor heard Boone approach until it was too late. As he reached for his gun, the horny fist of the prospector knocked him to the ground. Boone recognized the bandit. It was Big Bill Slavins, a quarrelsome miner who had been discharged a few days back. Boone disarmed him.

"Put those cans in their boxes and get them back on the burros and be quick about it, Slavins," said Boone. While Slavins gathered the cans and packed them, Boone thought hard and quickly. When the last box was once more securely on Old Jerry's pack saddle, Boone looked at Slavins.

"Get on your horse," said Boone.

Slavins swung into the saddle.

"I don't think you are a crook at heart, so I'm giving you a chance. I won't say a word about this. Get going now. This climate will be none too good for your health."

Slavins mumbled his thanks and rode away. Boone led

the string of burros back to the fork. He gave Bridget an extra large pan of oats that night. "Good little Bridget," he said as he patted her short neck.

WHAT HAPPENED?

Boone McBride had traveled for a long distance with his burro. Why was he so glad to see the O'Shea homestead? Why were the O'Sheas glad to see Boone?

At first the little burro had no name. How did she get her name?

One morning at dawn Bridget wakened Boone. What made Boone hurry to break camp? Tell how Bridget saved Boone.

Later on, Bridget did another wise thing to save Boone. How did she outwit the bandit?

THINK IT OVER

Boone was kind to Bridget. What were some of the things he did which show his kindness?

Bridget is as important in the story as Boone and the other human characters. What makes Bridget such an interesting character? Why does an animal make a good character in a story? Tell about another animal you think would make a good character in a story.

On the way to Moystons, Boone could tell a storm was coming. How can you sometimes tell when a storm is coming in your part of the country?

Jerry called Bridget a "Rocky Mountain canary." How do you think burros got such a name?

Boone did not turn Slavins over to the sheriff. Why do you think he did not have the thief arrested? Do you think he did the right thing? What are your reasons?

THE YOUNG CALVES

Robert P. Tristram Coffin

A hush had fallen on the birds,
  And it was almost night
When I came round a turn and saw
  A whole year's loveliest sight.

Two calves that thought their month of life
  Meant May through all the year
Were coming down the grassy road,
  As slender as young deer.

They stopped amazed and took me in,
  Putting their ears out far,
And in each of four round eyes
  There was an evening star.

They did not breathe, they stared so hard,
  Brother close to brother,
Then their legs awoke, and flank to flank,
  They turned and ran for mother.

A small boy in torn knickers came
  And caught them as they fled,
He put a slender arm around
  Each slender, startled head.

He never looked at me at all,
  I was not in his mind;
The three of them went down the road
  And never glanced behind.

"The Young Calves" by Robert P. Tristram Coffin. Reprinted by permission of the estate of Robert Tristram Coffin and of *The American Girl*, a magazine for all girls published by the Girl Scouts of the U.S.A.

WINKIE COMES THROUGH

Theresa Kalab

Tommy MacIntosh, a Scotch boy, worked during the Second World War with Mr. Raymond while his father served as a lieutenant in the Royal Air Force. Mr. Raymond took care of the pigeons which the British government used to carry war messages.

Tommy was proud of the pigeon Winkie. But Mr. Raymond did not think Winkie could be depended upon in a tight spot. However, when a call came from the government for two pigeons to go in a plane, Winkie and White Tail were the only two in the pigeon cote that could be sent out. All the others were already out on trips or resting from trips the day before.

As they were taken away, Tommy shouted:
"Happy landing, Winkie!"
Winkie and White Tail were delivered at the air base to a Beaufort bomber of the R.A.F. Before the crew took their places in the plane, they said "Good-by" to Flying Officer Duck, the mascot Captain Donovan had presented to the squadron. A ground man hung the container high in the cockpit. Here Winkie and White Tail were protected from draft and the smell of gas.

"Winkie Comes Through" from *Watching for Winkie* by Theresa Kalab. Copyright, 1942, Longmans, Green, and Company.

"All set, men?" Lieutenant MacIntosh asked as he settled himself at the controls. His glance drifted toward the container. He smiled tenderly as he thought of his visit with Tommy early that morning. Little did he know that his son's favorite bird was in that basket!

"All set, Mac," the navigator, Jerry MacDonald, replied as he saw the wireless operator and the gunner nod their heads.

The faces of the men looked grim as they thought of the job ahead. They were ordered to offensive patrol duty off the coast of Norway.

Contact! The propellers spun around. The motors started. The Beaufort bomber sped along the runway and glided gracefully into the pale blue sky. Higher and higher it climbed until now it looked about the size of Winkie. Then the plane disappeared into a distant cloud bank.

The plane climbed above the banks of clouds and sped swiftly along in a clear blue sky. It was quiet and peaceful, way up there. One could imagine a new kind of world, a world without strife. So Tommy's father thought, as the four fliers sailed swiftly through the sky.

Each member of the crew was busy with his own special job, the gunner alert, ready to spring into action.

At an order from the navigator, Lieutenant MacIntosh piloted the plane down through the cloud bank until he saw the North Sea spread beneath them.

Suddenly, from nowhere, a German fighter plane appeared. Then another, and another!

A shell burst near the Beaufort bomber. The explosion rumbled along the plane like muffled thunder, the sound covered by the roar of the engine. . . .

"Whew! That was a close call," said the navigator to Lieutenant MacIntosh, with a long whistle of relief.

"We were lucky this time!" Lieutenant MacIntosh replied grimly. But he spoke too soon.

Suddenly the engine sputtered, then stopped. A moment of tense silence. Lieutenant MacIntosh tried in vain to work the controls. His efforts were hopeless.

"We're in for it, men! Hold tight," he said quietly. "Jerry, have the dinghy ready as soon as we hit."

The wireless operator desperately tried to send an S.O.S. at the last moment.

With a resounding splash of the waves, the crippled bomber glided into the North Sea. The plane bounced, spank, spank, spank, spank, then rested quietly.

The crew were thrown from their seats by the force of the impact. Lieutenant MacIntosh tipped half out of the cockpit through the hatch.

"Jerry, I'm caught! Open the hatch!" he cried, trying to free himself.

Water was rapidly filling the plane. Water up to his knees, Jerry crashed the hatch open, holding firmly to the dinghy.

30

The water sucked both men through the hatch; the dinghy floated free. As they swam to reach the dinghy a shout was heard from the gunner.

"My parachute harness is caught in the guns!"

Paul, the wireless operator, his fingers numb with cold and shock, tried to free the gunner. Chlorine gas was forming in the cockpit, through the sea water coming in contact with the wireless batteries. Neither one of them spoke. They worked frantically together, hoping against hope that they would be able to pull the harness free before it was too late.

Meanwhile, with a swift steady rhythm, Lieutenant MacIntosh and Jerry swam through the bitterly cold water. They finally reached the dinghy and managed to inflate it.

"Here comes Jock!" they cried with relief. The gunner was swimming toward them. As they helped him climb into the dinghy, Lieutenant MacIntosh asked:

"But where is Paul?"

"He tried to save the birds. The pigeon holder was damaged when the plane hit the sea. One of the doors was forced open. As he lifted the container to take it into the dinghy, one of the birds escaped. It flew into the fuselage," he answered breathlessly.

Lieutenant MacIntosh waited to hear no more. He paddled to the sinking plane.

"Paul, Paul! Are you all right?"

"All right, Mac!" came a shout in reply. "We must save those birds. It's our only chance."

Lieutenant MacIntosh let himself overboard and swam through the hatch.

Paul was trying to coax Winkie to come to him. But Winkie, frightened, oil-soaked, and doused in the icy water, escaped his desperate clutches.

"Winkie! That's Winkie, Paul! My son Tommy's favorite bird!" the lieutenant exclaimed with great surprise.

"Winkie! You know me. Come here, Winkie," he coaxed quietly. But Winkie stayed out of reach. She had only one thought in mind. With a last final effort, she flew past Lieutenant MacIntosh and Paul, cleared the hatch, circled, and then flew off in the general direction of Scotland.

"There goes our last hope," said Tommy's father. "I shared the faith Tommy had in that bird. Mr. Raymond was right. She is too independent. Without a message, no one will know where we are."

"There's still this other bird," Paul said hopefully.

"I have no faith in White Tail now. She travels with Winkie. What she would do alone, I don't know," he replied.

Still clutching the container that held White Tail, Paul and Lieutenant MacIntosh climbed into the dinghy. As they settled themselves in the boat they saw the Beaufort bomber heave like a giant whale before its last breath, then disappear in the icy depths of the North Sea.

While the dinghy tossed on the restless sea, Lieutenant MacIntosh wrote a message on the thin strip of paper which he took from the little carrier attached to White Tail's leg. It was a gory and shaky message. His hand was cut and bleeding. He tossed the bird into the air and watched it disappear. That was the last the crew or anyone else ever saw of it. Darkness fell before White Tail could have reached the coast. As carrier pigeons cannot fly in the dark, it probably came down in the sea.

Throughout the night the shivering crew steered westward by the moon and stars. The minutes seemed like hours. They kept themselves busy, taking fifteen-minute spells at the paddles. . . .

In the meantime Winkie was flying as fast as she could toward the home loft. On and on she flew. Water, water everywhere. Her wings heavy with oil, she flew through clear blue sky, through dull clouds of mist. Sometimes she seemed to hang motionless in the sky as the wind whistled past her. Her great strong wings flapped with a steady rhythm.

Soon the rugged outline of the Scottish coast appeared, where the waves broke monotonously against the gray granite cliffs.

Over the city of Aberdeen she winged her way, past the bridge of Dee, the bridge of Don, and old Brig o' Balgownie. Past the River Dee, winding its serpentine course through Aberdeen until it spilled into the North Sea.

Flap! Flap! Steadily onward Winkie flew. Over purple

33

hills, over peaceful valleys, where little thatched cottages hugged the picturesque countryside.

Long shadows warned of the sun's approaching rest.

Now Winkie was nearing the city of Dundee. The sun looked like a crimson ball of fire on the horizon. Clouds tinged with gold and crimson hung suspended above the setting sun. The wind blew cold and chill. She was painfully tired, every muscle ached, but Winkie fought on through the gathering twilight.

Tommy was anxiously watching the sky, the lengthening shadows.

"Don't you want to go home, Tommy?" Mr. Raymond asked kindly.

"Not until it is pitch dark," said Tommy. "I am watching for Winkie. I know she'll come back."

Soon afterward, his heart gave a bound. Way off to the right he saw a pigeon, flying alone.

Nearer and nearer it came.

Suddenly it swooped and circled, then flew to the rooftop.

"Winkie! Winkie!" cried Tommy with joy. "I knew you'd come through!"

Winkie flew to the lighting board and sank down in the roost completely exhausted.

"Winkie, you're covered with oil! And no message?" Tommy opened the capsule and took out the thin piece of blank paper. Frantically he ran to the telephone and called headquarters.

"Tommy MacIntosh speaking."

. . .

"Number 531 has just returned with no message!"

. . .

Headquarters buzzed with excitement.

The telephone rang again in a few minutes.

"Tommy MacIntosh speaking."

. . .

"Yes, sir. Her flying speed is twenty-five miles an hour. She left here at ten o'clock, sir. Mr. Raymond? Yes, sir, I will call him."

. . .

"Mr. Raymond speaking."

. . .

"What! No, I shan't let him know. Please call me if you should have any word. I shall be anxious. Thank you, sir."

. . .

"Tommy," Mr. Raymond said gently, "you had better go home now." He put his arm around Tommy's shoulders. "I'll take good care of Winkie."

"But, Mr. Raymond, I can take care of her. I really don't want to go home."

35

His brows knit together in a puzzled frown. There was something strange about that telephone conversation, he thought. What was it that he shouldn't know?

Puzzled, he said good-night to Winkie, stroking her gently, and whispered, "I'm proud of you, Winkie. I knew you'd come through."

The next morning, bright and early, Tommy was at his post on the rooftop. He went through his routine duties, remembering his job as a ground man.

Winkie, quite recovered, was looking as saucy as ever.

In the afternoon the telephone rang.

"Tommy MacIntosh speaking."

.   .   .

"Yes, sir.   I will call Mr. Raymond."

.   .   .

"Mr. Raymond speaking."

.   .   .

"What good news!"

.   .   .

"His boy will be glad to know that he is safe!"

.   .   .

"Yes, sir."

.   .   .

"He always said that Winkie would come through with flying colors. I'll take my hat off to that bird."

.   .   .

"Tommy, I have some news for you. Your father and the three other members of the crew were saved by Winkie."

"My father!"

"Yes, he is all right, Tommy. The Beaufort bomber crashed in the North Sea yesterday, after an offensive patrol duty off Norway. Your Winkie was delivered to that bomber. Her code number and your information of her flying speed, plus a faint S.O.S., helped the aerodrome navigator to reckon where Winkie left the plane. She flew one hundred miles! A reconnaissance plane located your father and the members of the crew. Later they were picked up by an R.A.F. rescue launch."

Tommy's brown eyes were round as saucers with surprise and relief.

"That's not all, Tommy," Mr. Raymond said, with a twinkle in his eye. "You and Winkie are asked to a dinner at the mess hall, in honor of Winkie."

Tommy's face beamed with pride.

An R.A.F. car called for them, and they arrived in state at the mess hall.

What a wonderful dinner! Tommy had the seat of honor at the long banquet table. Winkie strutted up and down proudly in her basket, which was placed right in the center of the table. She at last had enough of her favorite peas.

Speeches, and toasts to Winkie, were made by the four men whose lives she had saved.

The climax of the dinner arrived. All the men stood up as Captain Donovan spoke:

"Tommy MacIntosh, I have the honor to present this token of appreciation to you—for Winkie—the bird that saved the lives of four men in our squadron."

The squadron gave Tommy a rousing cheer as he accepted a bronze plaque with the figure of a tiny bird flying over the sea. Inscribed on the plaque was the squadron's thanks to a gallant bird.

No one could tell who was the prouder—Tommy or Winkie. Newspapermen crowded around Tommy asking for details about her. Now Tommy could proudly tell the whole world how brave Winkie was.

WHAT HAPPENED?

Tommy's father was a pilot in World War II. In the beginning of the story, what had he been ordered to do? What caused the plane to crash?

The men knew the pigeons offered their only chance of rescue. Why did they think that? Winkie flew away without a message. Why did the men think this was so serious? Winkie flew back to Tommy. Tommy knew that something had gone wrong at sea as soon as he saw Winkie. How did he know this?

Winkie flew one hundred miles to get back to Tommy. How did the men at the air base reward Winkie?

THINK IT OVER

Can you think of a reason why carrier pigeons might not be as important today as they used to be? How do you think the bomber crew felt as they watched the pigeons escape?

Tommy was young, but he was trying to do his part in the war. He was accepting responsibility. What are some ways that children can help their country in time of peace?

We can all accept responsibility in school and at home every day. What are some things you can do at home to show that you are a responsible person? What are some things you can do at school?

Try to tell the story pretending that you are Winkie. You might begin this way: "I am a carrier pigeon. A boy named Tommy takes care of me. One day another pigeon and I were taken from our home and put into a bomber."

MEETING

Rachel Field

As I went home on the old wood road,
  With my basket and lesson book,
A deer came out of the tall trees
  And down to drink at the brook.

Twilight was all about us,
  Twilight and tree on tree;
I looked straight into its great, strange eyes
  And the deer looked back at me.

Beautiful, brown, and unafraid,
  Those eyes returned my stare,
And something with neither sound nor name
  Passed between us there.

Something I shall not forget;
  Something still, and shy, and wise,
In the dimness of the woods,
  From a pair of gold-flecked eyes.

"Meeting" from *Taxis and Toadstools* by Rachel Field. Copyright, 1926, by Doubleday & Company, Inc.

BULLIED BY BIRDS

Arthur Guiterman

The starlings have hatched in the nearest beech
A trio of nestlings, and bring to each
Twelve insects per hour. For Heaven's sake,
What horrible noises those starlets make!

Two swallows have built in our neat garage
A nest that is mud without camouflage;
Because of their little ones' appetites
We can't shut the door either days or nights.

A jay has appeared in his coat of blue;
He swears at our cat and the chipmunks, too,
And screams with that arrogant air of his,
"I'm boss of this ranch!"—and perhaps he is.

"Bullied by Birds" from *Brave Laughter* by Arthur Guiterman. Copyright, 1943, by E. P. Dutton & Co., Inc. Reprinted by permission of the publisher.

CAVALRY VOLUNTEER

Carl Glick

Nobody ever said Mickey was good-looking. He really wasn't. He had a long, thin body with his ribs showing plainly; long, thin, but straight legs; a long, thin neck. Believe it or not, he was a strawberry roan with a long but thin black tail, and a short but thick black mane. Right below his eyes was a splash of white. He was a funny-looking horse.

While the cavalry soldiers who loved Mickey couldn't say honestly that he was beautiful, they did make a lot of very complimentary remarks about him. They said, for instance, that he was very smart, had good horse sense, and knew how to take care of himself. They said he was tough, a good fighter, and adventurous, too. One of his finest traits was his unbounded curiosity. There was something glorious about Mickey, something proud in the toss of his head.

Where Mickey was born and who his father and mother were nobody ever knew. His early life remained forever a mystery. He was a wild horse, born somewhere on the

"Cavalry Volunteer" from *Mickey, the Horse That Volunteered* by Carl Glick, published by McGraw-Hill Book Company, Inc. Copyright, 1945, by Carl Glick.

open desert, and just happened one day to come along. As he grew older, he liked to go places, to do things, and to see things. He was always getting into trouble.

His story really starts shortly before the turn of the century, in the days when the Indians in Arizona were on the warpath, looting and murdering. The War Department sent, among others, Troop A of the Fourth United States Cavalry to put down the rebellion. This the Army did, quickly and effectively. When the Indians were once again confined to their reservation and told to behave themselves, Troop A was ordered back to its home station at Walla Walla, Washington. It meant a long and tiresome journey, traveling overland on horseback.

Off they started, a fine column of cavalry, with the Troop Commander riding at the head, and the guide-on flags fluttering proudly in the breeze. By day they skirted the edge of the desert. At night they camped in the foothills, where they could find a stream and a place to graze the horses. Then early in the morning the bugler sounded reveille and away the troop would go on their long ride home.

One day as the cavalry was moving northward across the Arizona desert, a wild colt about three years old came down out of the hills. He was thin, scrawny, and ugly. Seeing the long line of horses he neighed in greeting. Some of them neighed back in a friendly fashion.

What beautiful horses they were, too; sleek, fat, and well groomed. Only the finest horses in the country were selected for the United States Cavalry, and Troop A was famous for having the very best. Since no horse but a dapple gray was ever taken, Troop A was known everywhere as the Gray Horse Troop. The horses looked like brothers, and some of them really were.

It was almost an impertinence for this scrawny colt from the hills to neigh to these superior cavalry horses. It was even more impertinent when he came galloping down out of the hills, took a place at the rear of the column, and started to trot along at the end of the line. The Troop Commander, seeing this, said brusquely, "Run that wild colt back where he came from!"

"Yes, sir!" snapped Sergeant William Farlow.

He guided his mount out of the column, galloped along the line, and started to chase the strawberry roan. What a chase! Would the colt go back to the hills where he came from? He would not. Instead he completely circled the column and went right back to the tag end of the line. The more Sergeant Farlow chased him, the faster he ran. He could run rings around the fat cavalry horse Sergeant Farlow was riding.

When Sergeant Farlow would crack his long black whip, the colt, being agile and light upon his feet, would manage

to keep out of the way. He'd get just beyond the reach of the whip and then whirl and kick at it playfully.

"Hi, yi!" yelled the soldiers, laughing. They made all sorts of comments on Sergeant Farlow's horsemanship. The more they laughed, the redder Sergeant Farlow's face became. He simply wasn't able to get rid of this wild colt. No matter in what direction he chased him, the colt always managed to get right back again at the end of the line.

Finally the Troop Commander said, "Let him alone for the time being."

So back to his place in the column went Sergeant Farlow, feeling silly because of the spectacle he had made of himself. But he wasn't angry, for in his heart he admired the speed, dash, and high spirits of this wild horse. He wiped the sweat and dust from his eyes and said, "I bet that colt eats nothing but sagebrush for breakfast!"

Now and then Sergeant Farlow glanced back over his shoulder. There was the colt trotting gaily along. Occasionally he would toss his head in the air and give a friendly neigh. The sleek dapple grays would respond in a reassuring fashion as if they were saying, "How are you, pal?" It seemed to encourage the colt to continue to tag along, even if he wasn't wanted.

Sergeant Farlow said, "That wild horse should be named Mickey. He reminds me of a friend of mine—a fighting Irishman—who would never take no for an answer."

So day after day, Mickey followed the handsome cavalry horses. It was only too evident he wanted to volunteer— to be one of them—if only they would have him. But that was out of the question. A strawberry roan among those well-matched dapple grays would look out of place.

Some days later the cavalry came to a ranch that had a good corral. The Troop Commander decided that Mickey had better be left behind. Mickey's owner, if he had one, would in due time discover he was missing. Perhaps he would come and claim Mickey and take him back to where he belonged. If not, the ranch owner was instructed to turn Mickey loose a week after the troops had left.

As the cavalry rode off, Sergeant Farlow looked back over his shoulder. There stood Mickey, poking his long nose between the rails of the corral fence and gazing longingly after the soldiers. Farlow lifted his hand and gave Mickey a farewell salute.

"Good boy!" he said in parting.

In answer Mickey let out a heartbroken neigh. It wasn't a bit of fun being left behind. Then the cavalry turned a corner in the road and were soon out of sight.

Now a troop of cavalry riding homeward does not go at a gallop. If they jog along at an easy pace, better time is made in the long run, and the horses are not worn out at the end of the day. So slowly, mile after mile, the troop rode on back toward their station at Walla Walla.

One night, about two weeks after they had left Mickey behind, they had made camp as usual. The horses were staked out for grazing and the soldiers were sitting around the fire. Suddenly Sergeant Farlow, toasting his shins in the warm blaze, heard the horses getting restless. Here in the depth of the woods the night air was silent. Then came a faint and far-off neigh. Sergeant Farlow sat up. There was a friendly responding neigh from the grazing cavalry horses.

Sergeant Farlow rose and started back along the trail. Out of the darkness, sniffing as if he were looking for someone, came a scrawny strawberry colt—Mickey. His long legs were scratched, and his stringy tail full of cockleburs. Mickey saw Farlow and stopped.

He kicked his heels as if to say, "If you're going to start chasing me—I'll run faster than you can!" Farlow made no move. He just stood there waiting to see what Mickey would do next. Mickey cocked his head to one side. His gesture all too plainly said, "O.K.—if that's the way you feel about it!"

Then, paying no more attention to Farlow, he went on past him to where the horses were grazing. He started in eating with them just as if he had always belonged there.

"Can't we ever get rid of you?" said Farlow, grinning.

The way he figured it out was that Mickey, upon his release from the corral, had followed the horses' tracks until he finally caught up with them. He had covered the distance in half the time.

Farlow returned to the campfire and said to the Troop Commander, "Mickey's back!"

"How come?" exclaimed the Troop Commander.

"I think he likes us, sir."

"Well, don't spend any time chasing him away."

"Not me. No, sir. Looks like he wants to volunteer. And if he does—that's his business!"

So all the way back to their home station at Walla Walla, Mickey tagged along in the rear of the Fourth United States Cavalry. On their arrival at the military post he was turned loose in the pasture. Sergeant Farlow thought Mickey really needed fattening up. The pickings in the foothills by the desert had been poor. Here in the pasture was thick, nourishing grass and clover. Mickey loved it. It was the first time in his life he had ever had enough to eat. He was grateful to Farlow, too, for making this possible for him. Sergeant Farlow always spoke kindly to Mickey and spent many hours looking after him. In time Mickey followed Sergeant Farlow around as if he were his long-lost brother.

In the meantime, such being the army regulations, the Troop Commander made every effort to discover if Mickey had an owner. Certainly there was no sign of a brand of any sort on him. Letters of inquiry were sent to that part of Arizona where Mickey had first met up with the cavalry. But there was no satisfactory reply. Finally it was presumed that Mickey had deserted from a band of wild horses and had no owner. As time passed by, Mickey became as fat and sleek as the other cavalry horses.

Then one day the army inspector came along. The horses were all lined up, and as usual Mickey took his place in the rear. Among the handsome dapple grays he stood out like a sore thumb. When the army inspector walked along the line and came to Mickey, Mickey sniffed a bit. Then he stepped right up to the inspector and stood there as if asking, "Now what are you going to do with me?"

"Where did this homely horse come from? And what's he doing here?" asked the inspector gruffly.

Sergeant Farlow came forward.

"He may be homely, sir," said Sergeant Farlow, "but he's smart, willing, and can run like a streak of lightning. It's my impression, sir, that Mickey likes us and wants to volunteer!"

He told the army inspector the whole story. After Sergeant Farlow and the inspector had had a long talk, there was but one answer.

Sergeant Farlow promised, should the inspector consent, that he'd take Mickey in charge and that in time Mickey would be as well trained as any horse in the entire cavalry. He said that Mickey's being a strawberry roan wasn't a handicap.

The inspector agreed and ordered papers be taken out and Mickey duly registered as a member of Troop A, Fourth United States Cavalry. Now on papers of this sort the name of every horse, the price paid for him, the name

of the man from whom he was purchased, and the pedigree of the horse are recorded.

How could all these questions be answered in regard to Mickey? Nobody knew a single thing about Mickey save his name. Sergeant Farlow suggested that the spaces be left blank and that the only thing needed to go on Mickey's record after his name was—"Volunteer." That was the way it was. Mickey had the distinction of being the first horse that had ever volunteered for the United States Cavalry.

WHAT HAPPENED?

Mickey was not born to be a cavalry horse. Where did he come from? The men tried in several ways to get rid of Mickey. What did the men do?

At Walla Walla, Mickey grew fat and sleek. But when the inspector came he did not like Mickey's looks. In what way was Mickey different from the other horses?

THINK IT OVER

Mickey was a "volunteer." What does this mean in connection with the Army? What is another word that means the same thing?

The U. S. Army does not have troops on horseback today. Why do you think the cavalry has been disbanded?

When we talk about the "plot" of a story we mean the things that happen in the story. This story has a simple plot. The first thing that really *happens* is that Troop A is sent to Arizona to put down an Indian rebellion. What happens next? Be ready to tell the plot of the story—the things that happen—in the order in which they happen.

The story begins with a description of Mickey, but the plot does not really begin here. Why do you think the author began with Mickey's description?

49

THE RIVER BANK

Kenneth Grahame

The Mole had been working very hard all the morning, spring-cleaning his little home. First with brooms, then with dusters; then on ladders and steps and chairs, with a brush and a pail of whitewash; till he had dust in his throat and eyes, and splashes of whitewash all over his black fur, and an aching back and weary arms. Spring was moving in the air above and in the earth below and around him, penetrating even his dark and lowly little house with its spirit of divine discontent and longing. It was small wonder, then, that he suddenly flung down his brush on the floor, said "Bother!" and "Oh blow!" and also "Hang spring-cleaning!" and bolted out of the house without even waiting to put on his coat. Something up above was calling him imperiously, and he made for the steep little tunnel which answered in his case to the gravelled carriage-drive owned by animals whose residences are nearer to the sun and air. So he scraped and scratched and scrabbled and scrooged, and then he scrooged again and scrabbled and scratched and scraped, working busily with his little paws and muttering to himself, "Up we go! Up we go!" till at last, pop! his snout came out into the sunlight, and he found himself rolling in the warm grass of a great meadow.

"The River Bank" reprinted from *The Wind in the Willows* by Kenneth Grahame. Copyright, 1908, by Charles Scribner's Sons. Reprinted by permission of the publishers.

"This is fine!" he said to himself. "This is better than whitewashing!" The sunshine struck hot on his fur, soft breezes caressed his heated brow, and after the seclusion of the cellarage he had lived in so long the carol of happy birds fell on his dulled hearing almost like a shout. Jumping off all his four legs at once, in the joy of living and the delight of spring without its cleaning, he pursued his way across the meadow till he reached the hedge on the further side.

"Hold up!" said an elderly rabbit at the gap. "Sixpence for the privilege of passing by the private road!" He was bowled over in an instant by the impatient and contemptuous Mole, who trotted along the side of the hedge chaffing the other rabbits as they peeped hurriedly from their holes to see what the row was about. "Onion-sauce! Onion-sauce!" he remarked jeeringly, and was gone before they could think of a thoroughly satisfactory reply. Then they all started grumbling at each other. "How *stupid* you are! Why didn't you tell him—" "Well, why didn't *you* say—" "You might have reminded him—" and so on, in the usual way; but, of course, it was then much too late, as is always the case.

It all seemed too good to be true. Hither and thither through the meadows he rambled busily, along the hedge-

rows, across the copses, finding everywhere birds building, flowers budding, leaves thrusting—everything happy, and progressive, and occupied. And instead of having an uneasy conscience pricking him and whispering, "Whitewash!" he somehow could only feel how jolly it was to be the only idle dog among all these busy citizens. After all, the best part of a holiday is perhaps not so much to be resting yourself, as to see all the other fellows busy working.

As he sat on the grass and looked across the river, a dark hole in the bank opposite, just above the water's edge, caught his eye, and dreamily he fell to considering what a nice snug dwelling-place it would make for an animal with few wants and fond of a bijou residence, above flood level and remote from noise and dust. As he gazed, something bright and small seemed to twinkle down in the heart of it, vanished, then twinkled once more like a tiny star. But it could hardly be a star in such an unlikely situation; and it was too glittering and small for a glowworm. Then, as he looked, it winked at him, and so declared itself to be an eye; and a small face began gradually to grow up round it, like a frame round a picture.

A brown little face, with whiskers.

A grave round face, with the same twinkle in its eye that had first attracted his notice.

Small neat ears and thick silky hair.

It was the Water Rat!

Then the two animals stood and regarded each other cautiously.

"Hullo, Mole!" said the Water Rat.

"Hullo, Rat!" said the Mole.

"Would you like to come over?" inquired the Rat presently.

"Oh, it's all very well to *talk*," said the Mole, rather pettishly, he being new to a river and riverside life and its ways.

The Rat said nothing, but stooped and unfastened a rope and hauled on it; then lightly stepped into a little boat which the Mole had not observed. It was painted blue outside and white within, and was just the size for two animals; and the Mole's whole heart went out to it at once, even though he did not yet fully understand its uses.

The Rat sculled smartly across and made fast. Then he held up his forepaw as the Mole stepped gingerly down. "Lean on that!" he said. "Now then, step lively!" and the Mole to his surprise and rapture found himself actually seated in the stern of a real boat.

"This has been a wonderful day!" said he, as the Rat shoved off and took to the sculls again. "Do you know, I've never been in a boat before in all my life."

"What?" cried the Rat, open-mouthed: "Never been in a—you never—well, I—what have you been doing, then?"

"Is it so nice as all that?" asked the Mole shyly, though

he was quite prepared to believe it as he leaned back in his seat and surveyed the cushions, the oars, the rowlocks, and all the fascinating fittings, and felt the boat sway lightly under him.

"Nice? It's the *only* thing," said the Water Rat solemnly, as he leaned forward for his stroke. "Believe me, my young friend, there is *nothing*—absolutely nothing—half so much worth doing as simply messing about in boats. Simply messing," he went on dreamily: "messing—about—in—boats; messing—"

"Look ahead, Rat!" cried the Mole suddenly.

It was too late. The boat struck the bank full tilt. The dreamer, the joyous oarsman, lay on his back at the bottom of the boat, his heels in the air.

"—about in boats—or *with* boats," the Rat went on composedly, picking himself up with a pleasant laugh. "In or out of 'em, it doesn't matter. Nothing seems really to matter, that's the charm of it. Whether you get away, or whether you don't; whether you arrive at your destination or whether you reach somewhere else, or whether you never get anywhere at all, you're always busy, and you never do anything in particular; and when you've done it there's always something else to do, and you can do it if you like, but you'd much better not. Look here! If you've really nothing else on hand this morning, supposing we drop down the river together and have a long day of it?"

The Mole waggled his toes from sheer happiness, spread his chest with a sigh of full contentment, and leaned back blissfully into the soft cushions. "*What* a day I'm having!" he said. "Let us start at once!"

"Hold hard a minute, then!" said the Rat. He looped the painter through a ring in his landing-stage, climbed up into his hole above, and after a short interval reappeared staggering under a fat, wicker luncheon-basket.

"Shove that under your feet," he observed to the Mole, as he passed it down into the boat. Then he untied the painter and took the sculls again.

"What's inside it?" asked the Mole, wriggling with curiosity.

"There's cold chicken inside it," replied the Rat briefly; "coldtonguecoldhamcoldbeefpickledgherkinssaladfrenchrolls cresssandwidgespottedmeatgingerbeerlemonadesodawater—"

"Oh, stop, stop," cried the Mole in ecstasies: "This is too much!"

"Do you really think so?" inquired the Rat seriously. "It's only what I always take on these little excursions; and the other animals are always telling me that I'm a mean beast and cut it *very* fine!"

The Mole never heard a word he was saying. Absorbed in the new life he was entering upon, intoxicated with the sparkle, the ripple, the scents and the sounds and the sun-

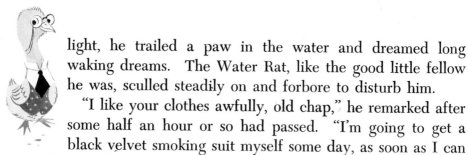

light, he trailed a paw in the water and dreamed long waking dreams. The Water Rat, like the good little fellow he was, sculled steadily on and forbore to disturb him.

"I like your clothes awfully, old chap," he remarked after some half an hour or so had passed. "I'm going to get a black velvet smoking suit myself some day, as soon as I can afford it."

"I beg your pardon," said the Mole, pulling himself together with an effort. "You must think me very rude; but all this is so new to me. So—this—is—a—River!"

"*The* River," corrected the Rat.

"And you really live by the river? What a jolly life!"

"By it and with it and on it and in it," said the Rat. "It's brother and sister to me, and aunts, and company, and food and drink, and (naturally) washing. It's my world, and I don't want any other. What it hasn't got is not worth having, and what it doesn't know is not worth knowing. Oh! the times we've had together! Whether in winter or summer, spring or autumn, it's always got its fun and its excitements. When the floods are on in February, and my cellars and basement are brimming with drink that's no good to me, and the brown water runs by my best bedroom window; or again when it all drops away and shows patches of mud that smells like plumcake, and the rushes and weeds clog the channels, and I can potter about dry-shod over most of the bed of it and find fresh food to eat, and things careless people have dropped out of boats!"

"But isn't it a bit dull at times?" the Mole ventured to ask. "Just you and the river, and no one else to pass a word with?"

"No one else to—well, I mustn't be hard on you," said the Rat with forbearance. "You're new to it, and of course you don't know. The bank is so crowded nowadays that many

56

people are moving away altogether. Oh, no, it isn't what it used to be, at all. Otters, kingfishers, dabchicks, moorhens, all of them about all day long and always wanting you to *do* something—as if a fellow had no business of his own to attend to!"

"What lies over *there*?" asked the Mole, waving a paw towards a background of woodland that darkly framed the water-meadows on one side of the river.

"That? Oh, that's just the Wild Wood," said the Rat shortly. "We don't go there very much, we river-bankers."

"Aren't they—aren't they very *nice* people in there?" said the Mole a trifle nervously.

"W-e-ll," replied the Rat, "let me see. The squirrels are all right. *And* the rabbits—some of 'em, but rabbits are a mixed lot. And then there's Badger, of course. He lives right in the heart of it; wouldn't live anywhere else, either, if you paid him to do it. Dear old Badger! Nobody interferes with *him*. They'd better not," he added significantly.

"Why, who *should* interfere with him?" asked the Mole.

"Well, of course—there—are others," explained the Rat in a hesitating sort of way. "Weasels—and stoats—and foxes— and so on. They're all right in a way—I'm very good friends with them—pass the time of day when we meet, and all that —but they break out sometimes, there's no denying it, and then—well, you can't really trust them, and that's the fact."

The Mole knew well that it is quite against animal-etiquette to dwell on possible trouble ahead, or even to allude to it; so he dropped the subject.

"And beyond the Wild Wood again?" he asked: "Where it's all blue and dim, and one sees what may be hills or perhaps they mayn't, and something like the smoke of towns, or is it only cloud-drift?"

"Beyond the Wild Wood comes the Wide World," said the Rat. "And that's something that doesn't matter, either to you or me. I've never been there, and I'm never going, nor you either, if you've got any sense at all. Don't ever refer to it again, please. Now then! Here's our backwater at last, where we're going to lunch."

Leaving the main stream, they now passed into what seemed at first sight like a little land-locked lake. Green turf sloped down to either edge, brown snaky tree-roots gleamed below the surface of the quiet water, while ahead of them the silvery shoulder and foamy tumble of a weir, arm-in-arm with a restless dripping mill wheel that held up in its turn a gray-gabled millhouse, filled the air with a soothing murmur of sound, dull and smothery, yet with little clear voices speaking up cheerfully out of it at intervals. It was so very beautiful that the Mole could only hold up both forepaws and gasp, "Oh, my! Oh, my! Oh, my!"

The Rat brought the boat alongside the bank, made her fast, helped the still awkward Mole safely ashore, and swung out the luncheon-basket. The Mole begged as a favor to be allowed to unpack it all by himself; and the Rat was very pleased to indulge him, and to sprawl at full length on the grass and rest, while his excited friend shook out the tablecloth and spread it, took out all the mysterious packets

one by one and arranged their contents in due order, still gasping, "Oh, my! Oh, my!" at each fresh revelation. When all was ready, the Rat said, "Now, pitch in, old fellow!" and the Mole was indeed glad to obey, for he had started his spring-cleaning at a very early hour that morning, as people *will* do, and had not paused for bite or sup; and he had been through a very great deal since that distant time which now seemed so many days ago.

"What are you looking at?" said the Rat presently, when the edge of their hunger was somewhat dulled, and the Mole's eyes were able to wander off the tablecloth a little.

"I am looking," said the Mole, "at a streak of bubbles that I see traveling along the surface of the water. That is a thing that strikes me as funny."

"Bubbles? Oho!" said the Rat, and chirruped cheerily in an inviting sort of way.

A broad glistening muzzle showed itself above the edge of the bank, and the Otter hauled himself out and shook the water from his coat.

"Greedy beggars!" he observed, making for the provender. "Why didn't you invite me, Ratty?"

"This was an impromptu affair," explained the Rat. "By the way—my friend, Mr. Mole."

"Proud, I'm sure," said the Otter, and the two animals were friends forthwith.

"Such a rumpus everywhere!" continued the Otter. "All the world seems out on the river today. I came up this backwater to try and get a moment's peace, and then stumble upon you fellows!—At least—I beg pardon—I don't exactly mean that, you know."

There was a rustle behind them, proceeding from a hedge wherein last year's leaves still clung thick, and a stripy head, with high shoulders behind it, peered forth on them.

"Come on, old Badger!" shouted the Rat.

The Badger trotted forward a pace or two; then grunted, "H'm! Company," and turned his back and disappeared from view.

"That's *just* the sort of fellow he is!" observed the disappointed Rat. "Simply hates Society! Now we shan't see any more of him today. Well, tell us *who's* out on the river?"

"Toad's out, for one," replied the Otter. "In his brand-new wager-boat; new togs, new everything!"

The two animals looked at each other and laughed.

"Once, it was nothing but sailing," said the Rat. "Then he tired of that and took to punting. Nothing would please him but to punt all day and every day, and a nice mess he made of it. Last year it was houseboating, and we all had to go and stay with him in his houseboat, and pretend we liked it. He was going to spend the rest of his life in a houseboat. It's all the same, whatever he takes up; he gets tired of it, and starts on something fresh."

"Such a good fellow, too," remarked the Otter reflectively: "But no stability—especially in a boat!"

From where they sat they could get a glimpse of the main stream across the island that separated them; and just then a wager-boat flashed into view, the rower—a short, stout figure—splashing badly and rolling a good deal, but working his hardest. The Rat stood up and hailed him, but Toad—for it was he—shook his head and settled sternly to his work.

"He'll be out of the boat in a minute if he rolls like that," said the Rat, sitting down again.

"Of course he will," chuckled the Otter. "Did I ever tell you that good story about Toad and the lock-keeper? It happened this way. Toad . . ." An errant May-fly swerved unsteadily athwart the current in the intoxicated fashion affected by young bloods of May-flies seeing life. A swirl of water and a "cloop!" and the May-fly was visible no more.

Neither was the Otter.

The Mole looked down. The voice was still in his ears, but the turf whereon he had sprawled was clearly vacant. Not an Otter to be seen, as far as the distant horizon.

But again there was a streak of bubbles on the surface of the river.

The Rat hummed a tune, and the Mole recollected that animal-etiquette forbade any sort of comment on the sudden disappearance of one's friends at any moment, for any reason or no reason whatever.

"Well, well," said the Rat, "I suppose we ought to be moving. I wonder which of us had better pack the luncheon-basket?" He did not speak as if he was frightfully eager for the treat.

"Oh, please let me," said the Mole. So, of course, the Rat let him.

Packing the basket was not quite such pleasant work as unpacking the basket. It never is. But the Mole was bent on enjoying everything, and although just when he had got the basket packed and strapped up tightly he saw a plate staring up at him from the grass, and when the job had been done again the Rat pointed out a fork which anybody ought to have seen, and last of all, behold! the mustard pot, which he had been sitting on without knowing it—still, somehow, the thing got finished at last, without much loss of temper.

The afternoon sun was getting low as the Rat sculled gently homewards.

WHAT HAPPENED?

Mole suddenly grew tired of working. Explain why he decided to stop work.

When Mole met the Rat, he found out many new things about the world. Tell about some of the things Mole had never seen or heard about before.

The picnic basket contained many good things to eat. How many of them can you name?

On the river bank, Mole saw some of Rat's friends. Who were they and why didn't they stay for the picnic?

THINK IT OVER

This story was written by a man who lived in England. Probably you found some words here which are not used very often in the United States. *Bijou* and *stoat* may be two of them. The dictionary in the back of this book will help you find out what they mean. What other words or expressions in the story were new to you?

The animals on the river bank talked and acted like human beings. When did they make you laugh? Did any one animal become a special favorite of yours? What made him your favorite? Read one of the parts about him or some of his conversation to the class.

What words from the list below would you choose to describe Mole? Badger? Toad? What are some words which would describe Water Rat? Look in the dictionary for any words you do not know.

shy	troublesome	thoughtful	neat	timid
rich	egotistic	restless	quiet	kind

EVER SINCE

Elizabeth Coatsworth

The first mules in America
    were brought, they say, from Spain,
a royal gift to Washington,
    sprung from a noble strain.

I like to think he eyed them
    with a farmer's thoughtful eye—
a little strange, outlandish, perhaps,
    but interesting to try.

"They'll have to get their landlegs first.
    Give them a week or two,
then let them plow the river field
    and show what they can do."

The mules looked obstinate and sleek,
    they pricked their heavy ears.
And they've been plowing ever since,
    for more than seven score years!

"Ever Since" by Elizabeth Coatsworth. Reprinted by permission of the author.

UNIT TWO

Out Our Way

THE NEW NEIGHBOR

Have you had your tonsils out?
  Do you go to school?
Do you know that there are frogs
  Down by Willow Pool?

Are you good at cricket?
  Have you got a bat?
Do you know the proper way
  To feed a white rat?

Are there any apples
  On your apple tree?
Do you think your mother
  Will ask me in to tea?

Rose Fyleman

"The New Neighbor" from *Gay Go Up* by Rose Fyleman. Copyright 1929, 1930 by Doubleday & Company, Inc. Reprinted by permission of the publisher and The Society of Authors.

THE BOTTOM
OF THE
BATTING LIST

Marion Renick

The school that Mike went to was a small one. It was so small that one year there were only eight other boys in his class, and when spring came every one of those boys said Mike should play baseball.

"But I don't like baseball. I don't see any fun in it," Mike would tell them over and over.

The other boys always said, "How do you know? You've never played it."

Mike would dig his scuffed shoe into the gravel of the schoolyard where the boys were holding practice. He would mutter, "Suppose I never have played. So what?" He would kick pebbles fiercely in all directions as if to show the fellows he was just as strong as they, even though he was so small for his age that they had nicknamed him Mike, which was short for microbe.

"So what!" Mike would say.

"So it takes nine men to make a ball team, that's what!" Chick or Red or The Moose would answer. "And we've got nine fellows in our room *and we're going to have a team.*"

Mike knew it was no use to tell them to get somebody else. Each class always made up its own team and they played one another for the school championship. Naturally, as Chick said, it was better to have a poor player from your own room than a good player from some other class whose loyalty you couldn't count on.

Chick was the captain. He was one of the best players

"The Bottom of the Batting List" by Marion Renick. Copyright, 1945, by *Story Parade*, Inc. Reprinted by permission.

in school, and, besides, he had a brother who played on the high-school team. It was Chick who kept saying, "Come on, Mike. You don't want to spoil the fun for the rest of us, do you?"

Mike said, no, he didn't. Then The Moose spoke up, tugging thoughtfully at his large ears, which had won him his nickname. "You don't want those smarty-pants 6A's to get ahead of us, do you? They're claiming the championship already."

Mike said, no, he didn't want the 6A's to get the championship, but he just didn't like baseball.

"You'd like it, once you got a bat in your hand," Chick promised, "and learned how it feels to knock out a good clean hit. One that, maybe, brings in a couple of runs. You'd like baseball after that."

"Would I?" Mike asked. He brightened a little, hoping Chick was right. He told himself that perhaps the reason he didn't like baseball was because he never had had a chance to play. Until this year there always had been enough other boys—larger and stronger than he—to make up the class team.

"Sure, you'd like it," Chick was saying. "Have you ever swung a bat? Here, try this one."

Mike said, yes, he had swung a bat before. He took the one Chick handed him, but he didn't say he had one exactly like it at home. And a glove, too. He had got them a long time ago but hadn't used them because nobody wanted him on a team. It was enough to make any fellow not like baseball.

He stood there swinging the bat from his shoulder and watching the boys. They were playing with two bases, and when a man struck out he played in the outfield until it was his turn to bat again. Everybody had to take a turn at bat, even The Moose, who was pitcher. Chick said the only way a player could score a run was by making a hit and getting to first base before the baseman got there with the ball. And although the pitcher and catcher usually came at the bottom of the batting list, because they were expected to be the worst batters on any team, still Chick wanted them to be able to hit a pretty fair ball if the team got in a pinch.

Chick now took Red's place as catcher, squatting behind home plate, while Red hit a low ball to left field and streaked for first base.

"You're up next, Mike," Chick said. "Now, take it easy and keep your eye on the ball—then swing the old bat right out and sock it!"

The Moose sent over a slow one. Mike saw he'd have to step clear across the plate to reach it. But he missed it, even then.

"Jeepers!" Chick yelled. "What did you strike at that for? A ball has got to come directly over the plate—no lower than your knees and no higher than your shoulders—or it isn't any good. Didn't you know that?"

No, Mike didn't know that. He thought there must be an awful lot about baseball he didn't know. He'd have to watch very closely and learn the best he could, because he didn't want to ask questions or the fellows would think he didn't know *anything*.

"I get it now," he said, stepping back in position for the next pitch.

This time he was sure the ball was good. It was coming straight over the plate. He put everything he had into his swing, expecting to hear the bat crack sharply against the ball. But there came only the soft thud of the ball burrowing into the catcher's mitt. He could not believe he had missed. He turned around and looked. Yes, Chick had caught it, all right, and was laughing in a friendly way.

"Mike, you've got to keep your eye on the ball. Do you know what you did? You shut your eyes when the ball came close. How can you ever see to hit? Now try again —and watch the ball until your bat touches it."

The Moose threw another. An easy one, right at the bat. But before Mike had time to think, his eyes had closed and the ball plunked into the catcher's mitt.

"Three strikes and you're out!" Chick called. "Now go over there in right field, back of first base, and try to catch any balls the baseman misses."

"I'd better go home," Mike said. "There's a lot of stuff I want to do there. Besides, I don't think—"

70

"Jeepers! Anybody's liable to strike out his first time at bat," Chick said. "Just wait till you crack out a good clean hit. *Then* you'll think baseball's fun. All you need is practice."

Everybody agreed that all Mike needed was practice. That made sense to Mike, too, so he stayed. Although he struck out every time at bat, he came back for more the next day. And the day after that. By the time they played their first game, he still couldn't hit and he still thought baseball wasn't much fun, but his team needed nine boys so he had to stay. Chick put him at the bottom of the batting list.

Chick himself headed the batting list because he could almost always be counted on to get a hit and reach first base; next on the list came the three best hitters; then a couple more who were only so-so; then Red and The Moose; and at the bottom of the list, where he could do least harm, was the poorest hitter on the team.

Mike nearly always struck out. "But you're getting better," Chick told him during their second game. "You're keeping your eyes on the ball now. Your only trouble is that you can't put enough steam into your swing."

If Mike thought that was because he was smaller than the other boys, he did not mention the fact. He only said, rather eagerly, "I'm a pretty fast runner, Chick. I'll bet I could *steal* bases."

"You can't steal first base," Chick pointed out. "The only way you can get there is to bat a good ball. Or to bunt."

"What's a bunt?"

"It's a—well—watch me the next time I'm at bat. I'll bunt one for you," Chick said.

Presently Mike was up, with Red on second base and The Moose on first. He knew that they hoped he would get a hit just this once. He spit on his hands, took a firmer grip on the bat and talked to himself. "Keep your eye on the ball," he said. "Sock it clear over that fence. You know you can do it if you swing hard enough."

Mike swung so hard he nearly lost his balance. But he didn't even touch the ball. Two more balls got past him the same way, and he went back to the bench. He was about to say that he didn't think baseball was much fun, when Chick spoke. "Watch this bunt, Mike."

The captain stepped up to the plate. Mike, watching every move, saw him turn to stand facing the pitcher just

as the ball was thrown. Halfway stooping, Chick had the bat out in front of him, parallel with the ground, holding the handle with one hand and the center of the bat with the other. As the ball hit, it popped dully to the ground. The catcher scooped it up and sent it to first base, putting Chick out. But, Mike noticed, Chick's bunt had given Red time to move up from second to third base. Red was now in position to come in home for a run, if the next batter got a hit. The Moose was on second.

"I get it," Mike said as Chick came back to the bench. "From now on, I'll bunt. If I can't hit hard and get to first base, myself, maybe I can help some other player to come in home."

"Bunting isn't as easy as it looks," Chick warned. "You'd better learn to bat first."

But from then on Mike was on the lookout for every bunt, trying to find out how it was done. He had been put in the right fielder's position for the same reason that he was at the bottom of the batting list. Very few balls ever came into this territory, so he had lots of time on his hands out there. At first, he had spent it thinking how dull baseball was, but now he was too busy watching for bunts to remember he didn't like the game.

He studied bunting for four or five games; he even practiced secretly, throwing a rubber ball against the side of the garage at home and trying to bunt it as it bounced

73

back. He thought he had mastered all the tricks of bunting by the time his team was ready for their last game—the game with the 6A's, the game that would decide the school championship.

Of course the 6A's were bragging and blowing as though they had won already, but Mike's team felt they had a fair chance themselves, although they did not say much. The whole school took sides, with a great deal of arguing about whether The Moose could outpitch the 6A man and whether a player like Mike was too big a handicap for any team to overcome. Both teams agreed to ask Chick's older brother to umpire. The game was that important.

Chick's brother brought another high-school ball player to assist him. Having these two older men there, marking off the diamond in the gravelly play yard, placing the bases in position, now and then consulting the baseball rule books that bulged their hip pockets, seemed to put the game into the big leagues. Even Mike, taking his starting position in right field, began to feel some excitement about baseball as he planned how he would bunt when his turn came.

But Mike didn't get to bat in the first inning. The 6A pitcher was too good. He sent a ball over the plate so fast that even Chick and the fellows at the top of the batting list couldn't touch it. Mike was worried. He knew he never could bunt a ball like that.

Neither team scored in the first inning, but the 6A's got two runs in the second, while Mike's team got one. In the third, the 6A's ran wild and brought in five runs, which so discouraged Mike, who was first up at bat, that he thought it no use even to try a bunt. He swung half-heartedly at the first ball, missing it by a mile. The second ball came more slowly and, after it passed, he realized he might have bunted it successfully if he hadn't been expecting one

too fast to hit. The third pitch was wide. But Mike had long since learned to strike only at balls that came over the plate, so he let it go by. One of the umpires yelled, "Ball one!"

Another ball came over, too low. "Ball two!" called the umpire. The pitcher was slowing down now. Or, Mike wondered, was he merely resting his pitching arm? After all, a smart pitcher doesn't waste his fast balls on a fellow who is at the bottom of the batting list.

"I'll show him," Mike muttered. "I'll give him the old bunt."

Then Mike had a crafty thought. Why throw away a bunt when there were no men on base? Why not go on striking out until the pitcher felt sure he had nothing to worry about when Mike was at bat? Then—

"*Then*—I'll show him," Mike said to himself. And struck out.

His team got in three runs that inning. The score was 7 to 4 in favor of the 6A's as they went into the fourth. Then Chick passed the word around to tighten up. So, with The Moose already on first base, Mike went to bat determined to do his best for his team.

Not until he stood at the plate waiting for the pitch did he realize how little he knew about bunting. Two slow, easy balls got past him before he was sure what he was trying to do. When the third ball came, he was ready with the bat in the correct position—but he forgot to slide his right hand out to support the center of it. At just the wrong moment the bat wobbled and let the ball go by.

As Mike returned to the bench he was telling himself baseball wasn't any fun. But he was remembering in the back of his mind how the whole 6A team had seemed to relax and go off guard when he came to bat. He was thinking, too, how to use his right hand to steady the bat. He smiled to himself.

The 6A's got one run in the fourth and one in the fifth. Mike's team got two in the fourth, which left them trailing, 9 to 6, when they went to bat in the second half of the fifth inning. Their first man up hit a single and got on first base. They were near the bottom of the batting list now, but luckily Red and The Moose each got a hit. That left all three men on base when Mike came up.

"Bases loaded," Mike said to himself. "Boy, what a spot for a bunt!"

He was too excited to let the first ball go by, as more experienced players sometimes do. He saw the pitcher raise his arm, and the instant the ball was in the air Mike had turned to face it, holding the bat across the front of him.

Plunk! The ball hit squarely. Mike felt a sharp, stinging pain in the fingers of his right hand but he didn't have time to think about it as he flung aside the bat and raced down the base line. The 6A's had been caught completely off guard. By the time the catcher had recovered the ball and decided where to throw it, Mike was safe. Red and The Moose had advanced to next base, and the man on third had gone home. Mike had brought in a run! He stood on first base and hugged himself with excitement.

Chick batted next. He was put out by the first baseman, but meantime Red got home. Two runs in!

The next batter struck out, and the one after him hit to center field, giving The Moose time to get to home plate. Mike, who had stolen up from second base to third, was right on his heels and got in safe, too. For the first time in his life, Mike had made a run! He was so thrilled and worked up and breathless, he didn't notice anything the matter until Chick exclaimed, "Jeepers, Mike, what happened to your hand?"

Mike looked. Blood was splattered all down the front of him, even dripping on the ground. He couldn't tell for sure how many fingers were hurt because his whole hand was covered with blood.

"Jeepers!" Chick said again in an awed voice.

Another man had struck out by that time and the inning ended. Chick's brother, taking one look at Mike's hand, brought the first-aid kit. But although the umpires discovered no broken bones and found that the injury was much more painful than it was serious, they decided Mike should have a doctor dress it immediately. "Better be on the safe side," they said.

"What's the score?" Mike asked.

"It's 10 to 9, our favor," his teammates told him.

"I'll keep on playing," he decided. "If I leave now we'll have to give the game to the 6A's because we won't have enough men to make a team."

"But the game is over," Chick's brother said, much to the boy's surprise. "You have played five innings, haven't you?" He brought the rule book from his pocket. He thumbed the pages and let Chick and Mike and all the 6A's read the lines he pointed out. There it was in black print: "It is a regulation game, if, after five innings have been played, the game is called off by the umpires on account of rain, darkness, or any other cause which stops play."

The other umpire agreed. "Certainly when one team has only eight men to put in the field, that is a cause which stops play."

"And five innings have been played, all right," Mike's teammates were declaring happily. "So we won—by one run. Your run, Mike!" They pounded him on the back and capered around, demanding of the 6A's, "Ho, ho, who're the champions now?"

The other team made a great fuss, but they had to admit the umpires were right. While they were still arguing, Chick, on his brother's advice, steered Mike off the baseball field and down the street to the nearest doctor's office.

Mike's hand was hurting more and more. He had to grit his teeth to keep from groaning as he tried to apologize, "I'm sorry I spoiled the game."

"You didn't spoil it!" Chick fairly shouted. "You won it! We never could have kept ahead of those 6A's for four more innings. You really won the game with your smashed hand. By the way, how did it happen? When you bunted?"

Mike nodded, a little grim and white about his tightly closed lips.

"I was afraid of that," Chick sympathized. "You have to learn to keep your fingers out of the way, where the ball won't hit them."

"I get it now," Mike said. He even managed to smile at himself, wondering how he had missed such an important point when he watched the other fellows bunting. Perhaps he should have asked questions, after all.

"But, Jeepers, it sure was a swell bunt." Chick's face glowed. "You picked a smart time to use it, too—with the bases loaded."

Mike tried to look modest, but he didn't feel modest in the least. He felt awfully proud of himself. He had won the game. Single-handed. Hadn't Chick just said so? Baseball *was* fun!

WHAT HAPPENED?

Mike thought he didn't want to play baseball. Why did he change his mind?

The other boys tried to help Mike learn to play. What were some of the rules they taught him?

Mike's team won the big game. What did Mike do to help win the game? Why were only five innings played?

THINK IT OVER

Mike was willing to play baseball because the team needed him. Why is it a good thing for people to be willing to work together? How can you co-operate with other people in things besides games?

Mike decided to bunt so that his teammates could make bases. How did this show good teamwork?

At first Mike thought baseball wasn't any fun. But that was because he couldn't play the game well. Why is it not a good idea to make up your mind that you don't like something just because you don't know anything about it?

A very good player sometimes wants to make all the star plays and get all the credit for winning. Do you think Mike was more valuable to his team than this kind of player? What are your reasons?

APRIL

Sara Teasdale

The roofs are shining from the rain,
  The sparrows twitter as they fly,
And with a windy April grace
  The little clouds go by.

Yet the back yards are bare and brown
  With only one unchanging tree—
I could not be so sure of Spring
  Save that it sings in me.

AUTUMN

Emily Dickinson

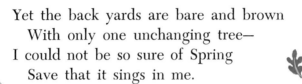

The morns are meeker than they were,
  The nuts are getting brown;
The berry's cheek is plumper,
  The rose is out of town.

The maple wears a gayer scarf,
  The field a scarlet gown.
Lest I should be old-fashioned,
  I'll put a trinket on.

"April" from *Rivers to the Sea* by Sara Teasdale. Reprinted by permission of The Macmillan Company.

"Autumn" from *Poems by Emily Dickinson*, edited by Martha Dickinson Bianchi and Alfred Leete Hampson. Copyright, 1914, by Martha Dickinson Bianchi. Reprinted by permission of Little, Brown and Company, publishers.

THE RANCH AT HEBER'S CROSSING

Mary and Conrad Buff

Dawn came. The dawn of a June morning in Utah. A bumblebee darted through the screenless window of a ranch house. After circling a small bedroom the bee darted out again, buzzing angrily. The sun rose above White Horse Mesa. Suddenly a ray of light struck a cracked mirror on the wall of the bedroom. It flashed back into the face of a sleeping boy, Peter Anderson. Peter flung his brown hand over his eyes as he half awakened. Where was he? He heard the sweet call of a mockingbird and smelled alfalfa. Then, as he heard Shorty shouting at the horses in the corral, he remembered. He was at his Uncle Orson's ranch in Heartbreak Valley.

Still drugged with sleep, Peter yawned, stretched his legs. His whole body felt stiff and sore, for he had ridden the fat mare, Molasses, daily for several weeks. It seemed to Peter, as he lay wiggling his toes, that he had been at the ranch much more than three weeks. He still recalled his mother's anxious face as she said good-by to him at the bus station in Salt Lake City. How hard it had been to keep from crying as the spires of the great Temple

"The Ranch at Heber's Crossing" from *Peter's Pinto* by Mary and Conrad Buff. Copyright, 1949, by Mary Marsh Buff and Conrad Buff. Reprinted by permission of The Viking Press, Inc., New York.

disappeared in the distance, and Peter knew he was leaving home!

When the bus finally let Peter off at Sharonville it was so late that everybody in the crossroads village was asleep. Only the coyotes yelped in chorus from the hills. Just how long the lonely boy lay on the cold bench in the darkness of the station, he never knew. But it must have been most of the night, for when he awakened it was getting light. A tall man in blue jeans and a red shirt was shaking his shoulder. His cousin Doug, whom he knew from a photograph, smiled shyly.

"We're sorry we are so late, or is it early?" his uncle had said. "We started from the ranch in plenty of time last night to meet you at the bus. But when we got into the canyon at the Narrows, a cloudburst upstream had sent tons of water reeling down the canyon. We couldn't get through. We had to wait and wait up a side canyon for the water to go down. It did at last. But the road through there is pretty bad and on our way home we'll have some tough traveling. Come on, Peter."

The three climbed up on the cab of the Ford truck awaiting them. Soon the truck was racing toward the mouth of a canyon walled on both sides by red, pink, white, and yellow cliffs. When they entered the canyon the cliffs were so high that they blotted out the early morning sun. The truck traveled in shadow. Wind and rain had carved the canyon walls into many shapes. Some looked like ruined castles, others like weird animals. Doug showed Peter a rock that looked like a motorcycle cop, another like a crouching bear, another like an eagle. . . .

Doug pointed to a clump of trees that looked as green

as emeralds in the gray plain that stretched as far as Peter could see.

"See those cottonwoods over there, Pete? That's our ranch.". . .

And that was only three weeks ago, he thought.

Peter's bedroom was now flooded with sunlight. The boy was awake. He leaned over the side of his bed and peered into Doug's bed. His cousin was still asleep. Peter slid to the floor. He slipped on his soiled blue jeans, his faded shirt, and the old cowboy boots Doug had loaned him.

"Doug, you lazy guy, wake up, you," Peter yelled.

Doug did not move.

"Wake up, Doug, you snail, wake up," he repeated.

Still Doug lay quietly. Peter grabbed a cup of cold water that lay on the table. Leaning over, he let the water dribble over Doug's face. Doug really *did* wake up. . . .

The smell of frying bacon and hotcakes drifted through the cracks of the door. Someone, probably Shorty, the hired man, struck a dishpan with a metal spoon.

Chasing each other, the boys dashed through the house, slamming the kitchen door behind them. The bathroom outside was a bench with two wash basins. On the log wall hung a wavy mirror and a soiled towel. Peter grabbed the

handle of an old-fashioned pump and jerked it up and down. Doug held a basin under the spout. The cold water gushed out. The boys dabbed their faces in the water, hurriedly scraped their unruly hair with a comb lacking several teeth. Then, shining and hungry, they walked sedately into the kitchen.

"Good gracious! Morning, you two cyclones," said Doug's mother, Aunt Martha, to Peter. . . . Uncle Orson had finished breakfast and was talking with Shorty, who picked his teeth with a toothpick. . . .

Shorty, the hired man, was the talker of the family. Aunt Martha said he opened his mouth and then went away and left it running. Peter loved Shorty. He said such funny things. When he went to take a bath, he said he was going to "wash out the canyon." Sometimes he would warn the boys in the morning, "I'm going to be all horns and rattles today." But Peter never thought Shorty was "all horns and rattles." He was always ready to help lasso a calf, saddle a horse. He knew about animals and insects; which snakes were poisonous, which ones were not; he knew where to find trapdoor spiders and he had given Peter a desert tortoise.

"Well, Half-pint, what's up for today?" inquired Shorty. He had named Peter Half-pint the first day he had come. Peter *was* small.

The boy, his mouth full of hotcakes, mumbled, "You know as well as I do, Shorty, that today I'm going to ride old Whiskers. You promised."

"Oh, so I did. No more lazy Molasses for you."

Peter had ridden the fat old mare ever since he had reached Heber's Crossing. Molasses was gentle and had never thrown anyone in her comfortable life. But she was fat and her trot was hard. Her colt, Star, followed her

everywhere. Molasses had him on her mind, too. When
Peter rode her she was always turning around to see if Star
was coming. He felt as if he were riding a merry-go-round.
Just the same, Molasses had taught him to ride. He had
learned to mount, to stop, to turn her right or left, and,
more than that, he stayed on when Molasses trotted, something hard to do when he rode bareback.

The cousins hurried through breakfast. There were the
usual chores to do before playtime. Uncle Orson was strict
about chores. The beds did not take more time than usual
to make, nor did the churning, but with three rows of
carrots to hoe, it was ten o'clock before the work was all
done. Then the boys raced to the corral.

Five horses were milling about in the dust. Molasses and
Star came at once to the fence, looking for something to eat.
Rosie, a glossy chestnut, was Uncle Orson's favorite saddle
horse. But Peter liked Danger, Doug's horse, best of
all. . . .

Whiskers, the young cream-colored horse with a little
mustache on his upper lip, was to be Peter's mount for
the rest of the summer if he could manage him. Peter
watched Doug saddle Danger and then quickly turned and
caught Whiskers by his hackamore before he could get

away. Doug held the reins. Peter threw on a saddle blanket, and a little saddle. As he tightened the girths, Whiskers blew up his stomach as usual. The boys mounted. Shorty let down the bars of the corral.

"Take it easy, Pete," he lectured. "Don't let Whiskers get his head. Hold the reins tight. He'll try to get the best of you. But if you start out right and let him know who's boss, you won't have any trouble with him later. Want King to go along?"

"Sure, come on, King," they called. King was happy and jumped and barked about the horses' feet. Peter held the reins and clamped his knees close to Whiskers' sides as they ambled along the dusty road.

"Where shall we go, Pete?" inquired Doug.

"Don't know. You know all the places. Anywhere you like."

"Let's take it easy then and ride up along the river a couple of miles, past Jed's shack. The road is level and you and Whiskers can get acquainted. Lots better than Molasses, huh?"

"I'll say so," sighed Peter. "He's easy to ride.". . .

They had ridden a mile or two along the dusty river road when Peter suddenly felt Whiskers tremble and jump sideways. At the same time he heard the whir of an insect. He grabbed the saddle horn. His horse whirled around like a top and bolted.

Doug called out, "Hold on, Pete. Don't let him get his head. Pretends he hears a rattler."

Whiskers circled and danced again from one side of the road to the other, and Peter thought for a moment he was going to buck. But the boy held firmly to the reins and clamped his knees against the horse's sides. After a few moments of dancing, Whiskers finally decided Peter knew how to ride. He quieted down and meekly cantered up beside Danger. Before long he forgot the imaginary rattlesnake.

"Trying you out," said Doug, laughing. "Only a horse grasshopper. They hiss like snakes."

"Horses sure are smart," added Peter.

As they rode along Peter pointed to a shabby log shack in the distance under a lonely cottonwood tree. "Is that Jed's shack you spoke of?" he asked.

"Yes, that's it."

"Who is Jed?"

"He's an old guy who lives there. He has a wooden leg · and scary eyes. Kinda crazy. A hermit. But sometimes he does come out of his shell and play for dances here in the valley. He can sure make his old fiddle sing. . . .

"He hunts in the hills with a gun and a gunny sack. All he brings back are pieces of colored stones and petrified wood. He shines up the stones so they're real pretty. When he's got a lot of shiny stones, he goes into town with the mail truck. Mom thinks he sells the polished stones to people that go through Sharonville."

King barked. Whiskers bent his ears forward and sniffed the air. Danger pricked up his ears, too.

"The horses hear something," called Doug. "Let's race."

They galloped along the road that followed the half-dry river. As they rounded a bend they saw a little animal struggling and moaning in the sandy bottom of the river.

"That's one of Jed's goats, I bet. Mired in the quicksand. Let's get her out," said Doug.

The boys slid from their horses, hastily dropping the reins on the ground. Being western horses, the animals stood still. Doug grabbed a coiled lariat from his saddle horn. He stood on the bank of the river, legs apart, and whirled the rope through the air. It fell neatly around the goat's neck. How Peter wished he could lasso an animal so surely.

"Come on, Whitie, pull, pull up your legs," cried Doug. But the frightened goat only coughed and bleated. Seeing the rope would only choke her, Doug stopped pulling and gazed around. The trunk of an old tree that had been carried down by a flood lay nearby. The tree trunk gave Doug an idea.

"Pete, help me roll this log."

The boys pushed the heavy log until one end rested on the bank of the river, the other close to the sinking goat.

Doug pulled off his cowboy boots and teetered along the log. Peter followed. Both boys were afraid of falling into the quicksand themselves. Peter held the rope while Doug leaned over and pulled up Whitie's front feet. The quicksand stuck like strong glue. Doug pulled with all his strength. Whitie's front feet were at last both free. Now she had strength enough to pull first one and then the other of her hind feet free of the deadly quicksand. Peter pulled on the rope to aid her. Then she followed the boys along the log and soon the three of them stood safely on the firm bank. King barked excitedly, trying to help but getting in everybody's way. Peter and Doug now led the muddy goat toward Jed's cabin. The door was shut when Doug knocked. No one answered. Just then Peter noticed an old man with a long white beard hobbling toward them, a stick in one hand, a gunny sack over his shoulder. It was Jed the prospector.

As he neared them Jed yelled angrily, "What are you kids doing with my goat, stealing her?"

He came nearer, and Peter noticed his piercing eyes and knew why Doug thought he was crazy. Although both boys were afraid they stood their ground as Doug answered, "We were riding along the river, Pete and I, and we heard something bawling. It was Whitie. She was mired in the quicksand. In another half hour she would have been buried alive. We pulled her out. She's awful weak now."

"Oh, so that's it," muttered Jed, ashamed of his bad temper. "You pulled her out?"

"Yes, we pulled her out. It was a job though. That quicksand sure sticks." Doug was anxious to go.

"So you pulled her out," repeated the old man slowly, even sorrier that he had suspected the boys of stealing Whitie. He put down the gunny sack. He fumbled inside it. Then, holding out two pieces of petrified wood, he said, "Found some pretty rocks this morning." Running his tongue over one of them, he continued, "See how pretty this'll be when it gets shined up."

Peter gazed at the rock. It looked like an agate marble.

"You boys come over in a day or so and I'll have these polished up nice for you."

"We will, Jed, sure we will," said Doug, anxious to get away.

Jed opened the door of his cabin. Peter saw a dark littered hole, with many tin buckets hanging from the ceiling in rows.

"Won't you come in and set a while and I'll play you a tune?" asked Jed, now very friendly.

"We'd like to, but you know how Dad is when we're late to meals," shouted Doug as he and Peter mounted their horses and raced away.

Peter was happy to see the green trees of the ranch house come into sight. Shorty let down the bars of the corral.

"Whiskers and I got along fine, Shorty," called Peter. "He didn't really buck, but he sure tried me out. And we pulled Jed's goat from the quicksand. Jed's going to give us some petrified rocks when he gets them shined up."

Shorty grinned and said, "The old man still got the gold colic?"

"Sure," answered Doug, "still thinks he's going to find gold some day and be rich."

"You're getting to be a real grissel-heel, Pete."

Peter did not know what a grissel-heel was, but he knew it was something nice so he nodded.

WHAT HAPPENED?

Pete's uncle and cousin Doug were late in getting to the bus station. What had delayed them?

Life on the ranch was different from Peter's life in town. What were some of the things that were different?

Pete's horse pretended he heard a snake. What was it that he really saw?

Jed's goat was in trouble. How did the boys rescue Whitie?

THINK IT OVER

Peter was lonely when he first arrived at Sharonville. Have you ever felt lonely when you were in a new place? What could you do to help new boys and girls to feel at home in a strange place?

When he first saw the boys with his goat, Old Jed thought they were stealing. He "jumped to a conclusion." What does this mean? Why is it a bad thing to do? Can you remember a time when you "jumped to a conclusion"?

Later Jed was friendly with the boys. How did he try to make up to them for his first feeling?

Shorty said Peter was "getting to be a real grissel-heel." What do you think he meant?

In this story the authors use many colorful words to tell what the country looked like. Description like this makes you feel you have really seen the place. Pick out some of the good descriptive words and tell what pictures they make you see. We call this kind of description "local color," because it pictures a certain locality, or place, which is important to the plot of the story. In "The Ranch at Heber's Crossing" why is the place important to the plot? Could the things that happened in this story have happened in a city?

UTAH

Hamlin Garland

Beneath the burning brazen sky,
The yellowed tepees stand.
Not far away a singing river
Sets through the sand.
Within the shadow of a lonely elm tree
The tired ponies keep.
The wild land, throbbing with the sun's hot magic,
Is rapt as sleep.

Strange that to me that burning desert
Seems so dear.
The endless sky and lonely mesa,
Flat and drear,
Calls me, calls me as the flute of Utah
Calls his mate—
This wild, sad, sunny, brazen country,
Hot as hate.

"Utah" from *Prairie Songs* by Hamlin Garland. Reprinted by permission of
Constance Garland Doyle and Isabel Garland Lord.

HERBERT'S WAVE

Hazel Wilson

When the Yadons' neighbors, the Barlows, were moving away, naturally Herbert, Pete, Donny, and Chuck were interested in the contents of the Barlows' trash cans, for they knew that people, when moving, often throw out things more or less useful to boys. There were two trash cans piled high at the back of the house, and the boys went over their contents thoroughly. . . .

"Guess we can just about finish our clubhouse with the things the Barlows are throwing away," said Herbert. "Say, here's a picture of a man leaning on a hoe and there's not a thing the matter with it."

"Any picture of a hoe makes me feel tired just to look at it," remarked Pete, who hated to dig in his mother's flower garden.

"Well, if we don't want it maybe we can trade it for something," said Herbert, putting the picture with the things to be saved. Then he picked up a small pasteboard box. "What's this?" he asked, and then read what was printed on the box, THE JIFFY HOME PERMANENT WAVE. Inside the box were two bottles full of milky-colored liquid and a lot of plastic thingamajigs. There was also a leaflet of instructions.

"Herbert's Wave" reprinted from *Herbert Again* by Hazel Wilson. By permission of Alfred A. Knopf, Inc. Copyright, 1951, by Hazel Wilson.

"Heave it back," said Chuck. "We don't want any of that stuff."

"It cost a dollar and seventy-nine cents without tax," read Herbert from the box. "And it's all here. There's nothing missing. It seems sort of a shame to throw away something not a bit used that cost a dollar and seventy-nine cents without tax. . . ."

Herbert was just about to throw the permanent-wave kit away permanently, when he thought better of it. "I wonder if this stuff really works," he mused. "I know some real straight hair we could try it on."

"You won't catch me curling a girl's hair," stated Pete firmly. "I wouldn't give any old girl curls for a million dollars, or a thousand or a hundred, anyway."

"Who said anything about curling girls' hair? What do you think I am?" asked Herbert indignantly. "Girls aren't the only ones who have hair in this town."

"We might try curling Old Man Jenkins' beard," suggested Chuck. "But I guess we'd have to knock him unconscious before he'd let us. And I wouldn't want to do that. He gave me a nickel once."

"My father's so bald it wouldn't be much use trying to give him a permanent wave," said Donny. "And what hair he has is already curly. And my mother doesn't approve of home permanents. She always gets hers at the beauty shop."

"I wasn't thinking of people," explained Herbert. "Animals, except for curly kinds of dogs, often have very straight hair. I'm thinking in particular," said Herbert, "of Creepy, the milkman's horse. His mane and tail are as straight as a yardstick. It might be sort of fun to give Old Creepy a permanent wave in his mane and tail."

The thought of Old Creepy with curly hair seemed

95

excruciatingly funny to Pete, Donny, and Chuck. They doubled up with laughter. Pete was the first to recover enough to talk. "Think Creepy would stand still long enough for us to curl him?" he asked Herbert.

"Creepy'd rather stand still than anything else in the world," stated Herbert. "He'd rather stand still than go any time. And if we give him some oats in his nose bag, he'll stand without hitching no matter what we do to him."

The boys forgot to go over the rest of the Barlows' trash, they were now so interested in giving Creepy, the milkman's horse, a home permanent. Herbert read in the leaflet of directions that hair had to be shampooed before it could be curled, so he went home for a wash basin and a bar of yellow soap. Chuck and Donny brought bath towels, and Pete came out of his house lugging a twelve-quart galvanized iron pail to be used for lugging water for the shampoo and rinsing. Herbert thought that warm water would be the best for the shampoo and suggested that Pete lug the pail full of hot water out to the barn where Creepy was kept. Pete said "nothing doing" to that. He was not going to lug a heavy pail of hot water half a mile or so for any horse. Besides, he said, the water would be cold by the time he got there. There would be sure to be a cold-water faucet

somewhere near the barn, he insisted. And cold water was good enough for any horse.

Creepy's barn was across the road and down a piece from the dairy, which would make it easier for the boys to do their beauty work without being disturbed. Nobody had ever told them not to give a horse a permanent wave, but they thought it best to keep what they were doing to themselves.

They found the barn door locked, but there was a window that Pete, the skinniest one of them, could be boosted through. He unlocked the door from the inside, and the boys made a beeline for Creepy's stall.

Creepy, as usual, was standing still. He was not interested enough even to look at his visitors.

Herbert and Pete set to work on the front end of the horse, while Chuck and Donny labored on the tail. Both ends of Creepy were doused with water, and the boys took turns rubbing on the yellow soap, as they gave Creepy a shampoo at each end.

Except for a shudder when the cold water first hit him, Creepy paid little attention to what was being done to him. A nose bag of oats kept him contented and occupied. He paid not a bit of attention to the shouts of "Back up" and

97

"Whoa," given by the boys working on him. Creepy just moved as he pleased. The boys sort of had to follow him all over the stall.

Chuck and Donny complained that it was harder to get Creepy's tail up on curlers than his mane. The hair was coarser and harder to roll, they insisted. Herbert, after finishing his half of Creepy's mane, had to help with the tail. "Pass me another curler," he ordered. "We might as well use all we have. We want to do a good job on Creepy."

At last all the curlers that had been in the permanent wave kit were on Creepy. He was quite a sight, standing there in his stall, with his mane and tail all rolled up on plastic thingamajigs. The boys had to sit down and laugh a while before they could go on with their work.

The boys dabbled the rest of the waving lotion on the curlers and fed Creepy a few apples to keep him happy while the wave was waving, or whatever the stuff did to hair. Then Herbert mixed some powder from an envelope in a pail of water and emptied half of it over the horse's head and the other half over his tail.

"That's supposed to set the wave," he said, getting out of Creepy's way, for the horse was showing his first objection to what was being done to him. He kicked and bared his teeth until Herbert soothed him down with some sugar lumps he had brought along in his pocket just for that purpose. It took quite a few sugar lumps and some more oats in his nose bag before Creepy would stand still again and let the boys touch him.

By that time, however, it was time to take off the curlers, which the boys did, being careful not to pull Creepy's hair. Then a final dousing with water, and the work was done. There stood Creepy, a big, bony white horse with his mane and tail in tight curls.

"I don't know if he looks better, but he certainly does look different," said Herbert.

"He's the funniest-looking horse I ever saw in my life," chuckled Pete. And he and the other boys laughed until they nearly cried.

Although the dairy was across the road and down a piece from Creepy's barn, the boys laughed so hard and so loud that Mr. Butterworth, the milkman, heard them and came to see what was so funny. He could hardly believe his eyes

when he beheld Creepy's curls. His face grew red and the boys were afraid he was dreadfully angry with them, but it turned out that he was on the point of bursting out laughing, which he did. "Whoever heard of giving a horse a permanent wave?" he kept asking between fits of laughter.

News of what the boys had done to Creepy soon spread around town and quite a few people came to look at the horse with the curly mane and tail. And they all came out laughing. They had never seen such a funny-looking horse in all their lives, they said, wiping their eyes.

Herbert felt quite pleased with all the notice being taken of Creepy's curls until some boys, not friends of Herbert's, called him "Herbert, the hairdresser."

Now the only hairdresser in Mapleton was a frizzy-haired lady by the name of Miss Eloise Bean, and Herbert felt that calling him a hairdresser was calling him a female or at least a sissy. Besides, he felt it was not fair for him to be singled out for insult, when Pete, Donny, and Chuck had done almost as much work on Creepy as he had. But, "Herbert, the hairdresser! Hairdresser Herbert!" were the taunts that met Herbert's ears, even when Pete, Chuck, and Donny were with him. It made Herbert fighting mad, and he did give one of his hecklers a black eye and would have sicked Mortimer on him if Mortimer had been a sicking sort of dog. But in spite of the fact that Herbert was handy with his fists, there were boys in town who went on daring to call him "Hairdresser Herbert" before taking to their heels. Herbert began to wish he never had heard of a permanent wave. Even some grownups teased Herbert about giving Creepy a permanent. "I hear you've gone into the beauty business," Mr. Mulock, the druggist, said, when Herbert went in for an ice-cream cone. It got so that Herbert dreaded to meet people on the street for fear they would mention permanent waves to him. It became a very sore subject with Herbert.

He was relieved when the circus made its annual visit to Mapleton, for that, he thought, would give people something else to talk about. Besides, the manager of the circus was a friend of Herbert's. Several years before, Herbert had presented the circus with his collection of small wild animals, for which the manager had been most grateful. The small wild animals were no longer small (wild animals do

grow so fast) yet Herbert always came to see them, although only the lion cub, now a full-grown king of beasts, seemed to remember him.

The circus train came in before dawn, and Herbert went to call on the manager and on his former pets before breakfast. He found the circus manager feeling most discouraged. His usually pink cheeks were pale and his black mustache that had turned briskly up at the ends the last time Herbert had seen him, now drooped sadly. "Like hair needing a permanent wave," Herbert thought, forgetting for a moment that he never wanted to have "permanent" mentioned, even in his own thoughts. But, what *was* the matter with his friend, the circus manager?

"The snap, the zip, the sparkle, and the gump have just gone out of the show," said the manager. But he took Herbert around the circus lot, and nothing looked as beautiful and attractive as it had to Herbert the year before. Even the hair of the beautiful lady bare-back riders looked limp and straight. And so did the former lion cub's mane and tail. But the former lion cub seemed to know Herbert and almost wagged its tail.

"I'm afraid he hasn't grown into a very kingly-looking king of beasts," the circus manager apologized. "With all that straight hair falling over his eyes, he doesn't look as fierce as a hairy dog."

Just then the circus manager happened to look up the road and saw Creepy on his way back to his stable after delivering the morning milk.

"What," asked the circus manager, "might that creature be? In all my days I've never seen the like."

"Oh, that's just an old horse we boys gave a permanent wave," said Herbert.

The circus manager stared and stared. Then he slapped his leg. "What this circus needs is some kinks put in instead of taken out," he remarked. "Before the afternoon performance I shall have every lady in the show go and get permanent waves at the beauty shop. But it would help, I think, if somebody curled the lion's mane. Do you think you'd dare tackle curling the lion's mane, Herbert?"

Herbert thought he dared to do almost anything, but he had never dreamed of curling a lion's hair. But he did want to help his friend, the circus manager, so, although he had vowed never to have anything to do with another permanent wave, he helped two experienced animal men wave the lion's mane. Even though the lion seemed to remember Herbert, it was thought best to tie the lion so securely that it could not harm him. And even with the help of the two experienced animal men, Herbert was relieved to get the job done. The lion's mane came out nice and curly. It made him look like another lion, a much smarter and fiercer one.

Then the circus manager waxed his mustache until it turned up again and not down, and the beautiful lady bare-back riders came back from the beauty shop with beautiful curly hair, and that afternoon the circus put on a very fine performance.

Everybody clapped when the curly-headed lion leaped through hoops and did other tricks that circus lions do. The circus manager, who was also the lion trainer, when he had a different hat on, came out three times and bowed at the applause. Then he made a speech publicly thanking Herbert for his help in getting the lion ready for the show. "This brave lad actually dared curl the lion's mane," he said, and the audience clapped again, this time for Herbert.

Nobody chased Herbert after that, yelling, "Hairdresser Herbert," for nobody dared tease a boy brave enough and bold enough to curl a lion's mane.

In a month or so Creepy's mane and tail began to get droopy again. And Mr. Butterworth, the dairyman, was so used by this time to driving a horse with curly hair that he came to Herbert to see about having Creepy given another permanent wave.

"No," said Herbert, "I shall never give another permanent wave to any man or beast under any circumstances. From now on the only wave I'm going to give anybody is a wave of my hand in farewell."

WHAT HAPPENED?

Herbert and his friends were looking for treasures in the trash cans. Finally they found the permanent-wave set. What did Chuck suggest they do with it? Herbert had a better idea. What was it?

At first Creepy was quiet. Later he acted as if he were tired of being made beautiful. What did the boys give Creepy to make him happy?

Herbert was very pleased with all the notice being taken of Creepy's curls until something happened. What made Herbert change his mind? Then the circus came to town, and Herbert had another job. What had happened to the circus? Tell how Herbert helped.

THINK IT OVER

What do you think might have happened in this story if a group of girls had found the permanent-wave set instead of Herbert and his friends? Could you write a story with girls as characters?

Many unexpected things happen in this story. Unexpected out-of-place things often make us laugh. This is one kind of *humor*. What were some of the things that made this story funny?

CITY LIGHTS

Rachel Field

Into the endless dark
The lights of the buildings shine,
Row upon twinkling row,
Line upon glistening line.
Up and up they mount
Till the tallest seems to be
The topmost taper set
On a towering Christmas tree.

AT LA GUARDIA FIELD

Arthur Guiterman

I would not be the prideful plane
  Bazooming as it flies
Above the rugged mountain chain,
  Across the starry skies.

I'd rather be the little truck
  That on the parking space
Will grab that airplane by the tail
  And put it in its place.

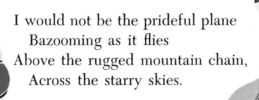

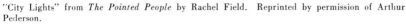

"City Lights" from *The Pointed People* by Rachel Field. Reprinted by permission of Arthur Pederson.
"At La Guardia Field" from *Brave Laughter* by Arthur Guiterman. Copyright, 1943, by E. P. Dutton & Co., Inc.

BOOM—BANG—WHAM!

Sterling North

Zeke's pet pig, Greased Lightning, caused trouble on the farm. He broke through fences and destroyed crops. Zeke's father decided to sell the pig to The Fat Man who ran the greased-pig race at the County Fair. Zeke secretly planned to go to the fair and try to win Greased Lightning back again.

Cherry Valley was having a real Fourth of July.

The cannon crackers went BOOM!

The little giants went Bang!

And the lady crackers went *pop, pop.*

Firecrackers that fizzled were broken in two to make a pair of "cats and dogs" which hissed at each other as the powder burned.

Red "spit devils" on the sidewalk crackled and sputtered under boys' heels.

And the torpedoes thrown hard against a brick wall made a big—B-O-O-M!

Long before breakfast, Cherry Valley was in an uproar.

When Zeke got to town he went to the livery stable. As a special favor, the livery stable man put his pony in one of the stalls for the day.

For over an hour, he almost forgot about Greased

"Boom-Bang-Wham!" from *Greased Lightning* by Sterling North. Reprinted by permission of Holt, Rinehart & Winston, Inc.

Lightning, he was so excited about the Fourth of July.

"I wish I had a cap gun, or some two-inchers, or even a penny package," Zeke said sadly to the livery stable man.

"How would you like to earn a dime?"

"Gee," Zeke said, "a whole dime?"

"Pitch down some hay for the horses, and feed 'em their oats," the man said, "but look out for the piebald mare. She's a kicker."

Fifteen minutes later, with a bright, new, shiny dime clutched in his hand, Zeke was shopping for firecrackers.

"Don't get burned," the firecracker-man said.

"I won't," Zeke promised.

Now for some fun, he thought. But before he had blown off half his supply, he saw, far away down the street, his father coming with the light spring wagon. He hurriedly drank a glass of the free lemonade that was being given away at a red-white-and-blue booth. Then under the band-stand he found a fine place from which he could see everything.

Zeke's father tied his horses to the nearby hitching rail. Several hours passed but The Fat Man didn't appear, so Zeke watched from his safe place all the excitement of the square.

First there was the parade led by the band in bright blue uniforms, the brass horns gleaming in the sun. Then came two companies of war veterans with a drummer and a great American flag.

Next came the mayor in the town's only automobile. Small boys on decorated bicycles shouted loudly above the blare of the band.

Following the mayor were all the fancy floats drawn by horses whose manes were entwined with red, white, and blue ribbons. The girls on the floats wore white dresses with red sashes and blue hair ribbons. They squealed when firecrackers went off too near.

It was all a wonderful sight. If Zeke hadn't been worrying about his pig, it would have been the biggest day of his life.

But now The Fat Man came puffing through the crowd to buy Greased Lightning. He reached in his pocket for his wallet and handed Zeke's father a ten-dollar bill.

"No, no, no," Zeke whispered, his heart beating wildly. But he knew that nothing he could do would stop the sale of his pig.

About ten o'clock the three-legged races, the horseshoe-pitching contests, and the pie-eating marathons got under way. And then came the awful moment:

"Greased-pig contest!" shouted The Fat Man.

"Oh boy, oh boy!" screamed all the youngsters of Pike County.

"His name's Greased Lightning!" shouted The Fat Man. "Fastest, slipperiest hog ever seen in these parts!"

"Let us at 'im!" screeched the excited boys.

But Zeke, now crawling out from beneath the bandstand, thought that his heart would stop beating. He saw his beloved pig, his own Greased Lightning, dragged from his crate. Rough hands smeared him with great lumps of lard. He heard his frightened squeals and saw his useless struggles.

Then, torn between fear and joy, Zeke prepared for the battle. He hitched up his pants, retied his shoelaces, and rubbed his hands in the dirt. He spat on the ground and drew a circle around it.

"Affey ke daffey."

Then he counted backwards from seven just for good luck.

In the mob of boys lined up for the race, all somewhat dirty and nine-to-twelvish, any boy named Zeke might have passed unnoticed even by his own father. So many pie-smeared faces and bright, eager eyes. So many pairs of brown legs and brown arms looking almost alike.

The boys were breathing hard and jostling and elbowing for the best positions. They were whistling between their fingers and making catcalls. Zeke wondered if he could ever outrun some of the bigger boys looking almost six feet tall. What chance did he have against a mob like this?

Two big tears welled up in the corners of his eyes, and

he brushed them away fiercely with his clenched and dirty fists.

"The boy who gets him can keep him," The Fat Man was saying. "Isn't that right, Eb?"

"I got my ten dollars," Eb said. "It's not my pig. But that's the rules. The kid who gets that pig can keep him. A bargain's a bargain."

A moment later, at a shot from the starter's gun, they were off. Whee! Around the courthouse they raced, over the beds of canna lilies, under the Civil War cannon and over the neat pile of cannon balls, into the barberry bushes and out again . . . torn shirts, scratched elbows . . . then through the lawn sprayer—loud shrieks as the cold water doused them.

Whoops! Over went a baby buggy—luckily, an empty one. There went the banana cart, scattering yellow fruit among the screaming spectators. Half a hundred boys raced on.

At first the bigger boys were way ahead of Zeke. His mouth got hot and dry and his side hurt, but he pumped away as fast as his legs would carry him around and around and around the courthouse after his pig.

Once a big, red-headed boy had Greased Lightning in his arms. But the pig was so frightened (and so slippery) that at last he broke away and all the youngster had was a thick coating of lard.

People were shouting and laughing until they cried, but Zeke and Greased Lightning were running and fighting for their very lives.

And then Zeke had a bright idea. If he could cut behind that clump of lilac bushes and head him off! And now, with a burst of speed, he was within ten feet of the pig. Zeke made a flying tackle—and hung on tight.

"Lightnin', Lightnin', Lightnin'!" he sobbed. And Lightning, hearing Zeke's voice, gave a squeal of joy and stopped struggling.

Sssssss—BOOM—ahhhhh!

A sky rocket sizzled up into the evening sky. A very tired boy and a very tired pig were sitting in the light spring wagon watching the fireworks display begin. Pinwheels, sparklers, red fire, and Roman candles.

"Gee, Pop! Look at that one!" shouted Zeke. He squeezed his greasy pig in excitement. And a very tired pig was thinking to himself, "Now, I'll be the best pig in the world, I certainly will. And I'll never, never, never . . . well, hardly ever. . . ."

He had heard Zeke's father say, "A bargain's a bargain, Son."

And then he heard Zeke say, "Maybe I can help mend your fences, Pop."

And Zeke's father had said, "I'll need all the help I can get, Son. Looks like we're going to have that pig around for the rest of our natural lives."

BOOOOOOM!

Greased Lightning trembled in fright as a big aerial bomb exploded overhead, flooding the sky with a fountain of stars. Even Zeke's lazy pony, who was tied to the back of the light spring wagon, reared up in terror.

"We'd better be gettin' along home," Zeke's father said.

"Aw, gee, Pop—" Zeke started to say, but suddenly he knew that he didn't mind going home before the fireworks were over. He was hungry enough to eat raw bear with bread-and-butter pickles!

When they finally turned in at the gate, Zeke's mother came hurrying to meet them with a lantern.

"Oh, Zeke, I was so worried!" she cried.

"Look, Mom, we're bringing home Greased Lightning."

"I hoped you would."

"And—" said Zeke breathlessly, "we saw a lot of fireworks —Roman candles and rockets that went BOOOM—and oh, Mom, I'm so hungry!"

"I've fixed the best meal you ever ate," his mother smiled happily. "I've been keeping it hot for you for hours. Roast duck and dressing!"

"Gee, Mom, can I have two helpings—and one for Greased Lightnin'?"

"Can you beat that, Martha!" Zeke's father grinned. "Roast duck for a pig?"

"Well, just this once," Zeke's mother said.

WHAT HAPPENED?

Zeke went to the fair in secret. What had happened to make him do such a thing?

Zeke wanted more than anything in the world to get his pig back, but catching the pig was not easy. What had been done to Lightning to make him hard to catch? How did Zeke finally catch Lightning?

Zeke was glad when his father said, "A bargain's a bargain." He knew his father would not take the pig away again. What did Zeke say he would do to help his father?

THINK IT OVER

This story tells about a good old-fashioned Fourth of July. Close your eyes and describe the things you remember. Was this celebration different from the way you celebrate July 4th? How was it different?

Zeke did some things for luck before he started in the race. He spat on the ground and drew a circle around it. He counted backwards from seven. These are old-time superstitions. Have you heard about any other superstitions? How do you think such ideas began?

Boys and girls like this story because it has "suspense"— that is, it keeps you wondering what will happen. We keep reading to find out if Zeke gets his pig back. What other stories have you read lately that have suspense in them? What television or radio programs do you listen to that have suspense? Tell about the suspense in some of them.

114

UNIT THREE
Fancy Free

THE STARLIGHTER

When the bat's on the wing and the bird's in the tree,
Comes the old Starlighter, whom none may see.

First in the West where the low hills are,
He touches his wand to the Evening Star.

Then swiftly he runs on his rounds on high
Till he's lit every lamp in the dark blue sky.

Arthur Guiterman

"The Starlighter" from the book *Gaily the Troubadour* by Arthur Guiterman. Copyright, 1936, by E. P. Dutton & Co., Inc. Reprinted by permission of the publishers.

BERTRAM AND THE
MAGIC WAND

Paul T. Gilbert

THE GREAT
MARVO

From his seat in the front row at the Opera House, Bertram kept his eye on the Great Marvo as he pulled rabbits out of people's coat collars and made goldfish suddenly appear in empty bowls. Bertram watched even more closely as Marvo capped his performance by changing a lady into a tiger. It was all in the way in which the magician held his wand. Bertram was sure that if he had a magic wand, he, too, could perform that trick.

So he saved his pennies. When he had saved enough pennies, he went to the drugstore and bought a magic wand. The wand was made of tin. It looked something like a peashooter. Bertram showed the wand to George Fish.

"What are you going to do with it?" asked George. "Shoot peas?"

"No," said Bertram. "I'm going to change a lady into a tiger, the way Marvo did. Then I'll give a show and charge ten pins admission."

George whistled. "What lady," he asked, "is going to let you change her into a tiger? One of your aunts?"

"No," said Bertram. "I thought maybe I'd get Ginny Banning to take the part of the lady. She could dress up in fancy clothes, you know."

"I wouldn't be too sure about that," said George. "Ginny might have her own ideas about being changed into a tiger. But how do you know that you can do that trick?"

"I watched Marvo."

"But wouldn't you have to practice?"

"Bertram and the Magic Wand" reprinted by permission of Dodd, Mead & Company from *Bertram and His Marvelous Adventures* by Paul T. Gilbert. Copyright, © 1951, by Paul T. Gilbert.

"Well, maybe," said Bertram. "Of course I'd practice on easy tricks first, like pulling rabbits out of hats or making goldfish."

George whistled again. "Suppose you coaxed Ginny into letting you turn her into a tiger, you'd want to have a pretty strong cage, wouldn't you?"

"I could make one out of a drygoods box," said Bertram.

"Even at that," said George, "things might go wrong. Suppose you couldn't change her back into a girl again?"

"Oh, I guess there wouldn't be any trouble about that," said Bertram. "The hardest part would be getting her into the cage."

"Especially if she got stubborn," said George.

While he was making the cage, Bertram kept figuring how he could bring up the subject of tigers before Ginny. He figured that it would be safest to try to coax her into the cage. He wouldn't tell her why he wanted her to go into it. He might put a candy bar in it for bait.

But if Ginny happened to be stubborn, as she often was, Bertram might sneak up behind her and wave his wand and change her into a tiger when she didn't expect it. Only in that case, of course, it would have to be indoors, and he would have to be ready to jump out of the way before Ginny could pounce on him. She wouldn't be any too tame, Bertram figured, especially if she were taken by surprise. To get the tiger into the cage, if the trick had to be done that way, was another problem. Bertram decided to try coaxing first. And he knew for one thing that he could count on Ginny's curiosity.

As he was nailing the last slat on his cage, Ginny came clumping by on her roller skates.

"Hello," she said. "What are you making?"

"A tiger's cage," said Bertram. "Want to get in it?"

"Not me," said Ginny.

"Listen," said Bertram. "I bet you can't guess what I've got."

"What?" asked Ginny.

"A magic wand."

"Oh," said Ginny. "Is that all?"

"I'm going to give a magic show. And if you want to be in it, I'll give you half the admission fee."

"Pins!" said Ginny scornfully.

"Listen. All you'd have to do would be to crawl into the cage. I'll put in a candy bar . . ."

"Me! Crawl into a cage!" snapped Ginny. "Not for twenty candy bars. I know what you're up to." And Ginny dashed away.

This was none too encouraging. But Bertram was not one to give up easily. He would turn Ginny into a tiger yet— when she least expected it.

That evening after supper, Bertram practiced with his magic wand. He practiced easy tricks at first. He found an empty bowl and poured some water into it. Then he waved his wand, and presto! three goldfish were swimming around in the bowl. He took his daddy's hat and pulled three rabbits out of it. Two of the rabbits scampered away, but one crept back into the hat and hid there.

The next morning when Bertram's daddy tried to put on his hat, he felt something scratching the top of his head. He thought at first it was a cat. When he took off the hat, he was surprised to see a rabbit tumble out of it. Bertram was sure by this time that he could do the tiger trick.

Early that afternoon, Ginny came over to his house to tell him about Peggy Linder's house party to which they were both invited. The party was to be at Peggy's country home, and it was to last over Saturday and Sunday.

"I've got some new goldfish," said Bertram. "Want to see them? They are in the dining room." It was there that Bertram had left his wand when he had set the goldfish bowl on the sideboard.

Ginny, not suspecting anything, followed him into the dining room. She thought the goldfish were pretty. "Well, I've got to go," she said. "You don't have to dress up for the party. I'll see you later."

"Wait a minute," said Bertram. He was looking for his wand. But the wand was gone! Ginny was halfway to the door when Baby Sam, Bertram's little brother, came creeping into the room. Held tight in one of his chubby hands was Bertram's magic wand. It had rolled onto the floor. Baby Sam had found it and had been cutting his teeth on it.

121

"Da," he said, and he began waving the wand.

"No, Baby Sam. Give it to big brother," said Bertram anxiously.

"Da."

Then it happened! With a frightened little squeak Ginny suddenly vanished.

And in her place stood a porcupine! Baby Sam was waving the wand happily. He banged it on the floor and crowed with delight. He was pleased with himself because he had just made a porcupine.

Then suddenly Bertram felt himself changing into a pig, the ears first and finally the curly little tail. It had all happened in less than a second.

Bertram and Ginny stood glaring at each other. Baby Sam, frightened at last, let out a howl. He dropped the wand and it rolled under the table. Ginny squealed and bristled. Her quills stood out until she looked like a chestnut burr.

"Now you've done it," she said. "I might have known." And rattling her quills she rushed at Bertram.

Bertram grunted and turned tail. He dashed around the table and knocked over the goldfish bowl. But Ginny was right on his heels, and Baby Sam was howling louder than ever. All this howling and grunting and crashing brought Bertram's mama from upstairs.

"Shoo!" she said. "How did you get in here, you nasty things? And what do you mean by scaring Baby Sam?"

Bertram and Ginny had backed into a corner. Bertram tried to explain, but he could only grunt. Ginny was too scared to say a word. Bertram's mama scooped up the goldfish and put them back in the bowl. Then she picked up Baby Sam and cuddled him.

"There, there," she said. "Don't cry. Mama will chase

the horrid things away." So she took a broom and shooed Bertram and Ginny outdoors.

Out in the back yard they faced each other again. Both were crying now.

"Well, I like that," sobbed Ginny. "I came over to your house to do you a favor, and this is what I get for it. Now I can't go to the party. And I want my clothes."

"Well, it isn't my fault," answered Bertram. "I'm in as bad a fix as you are. If you had let me turn you into a tiger . . ."

"So that's what you were up to, was it?" said Ginny. So she went home and scratched at the back door. But when her mama came and saw a porcupine, she slammed the door in Ginny's face.

"Mama!" cried Ginny. "Let me in! It's me—Ginny!"

"Nonsense," said her mama. "Ginny has gone to a party. She won't be home until Monday. Go away now and don't let me catch you around here again."

So Ginny crawled into the doghouse, and slept in the doghouse all night.

Bertram waited a while, then pawed at the kitchen door, and said, "Let me in!"

"Go away," said Bertram's mama. "I don't want you around."

"But it's me—Bertram!"

"Nonsense. I heard Ginny Banning say something about a house party. Bertram has probably gone to it when he should have been cleaning the basement. I don't expect him home until Monday. Now scat!"

"But mama," whined Bertram. "I'm hungry."

"Well, then, if you're hungry, here are some slops." And she threw him some potato peelings, and was about to slam the door when Bertram found his voice again.

"Listen, mama. Baby Sam picked up my magic wand and cut his teeth on it. He got it out of order and changed me into a pig. It was meant for tigers."

"As if he could!" said Bertram's mama. "You'll be telling me next that he changed Ginny Banning into that porcupine."

124

"He did that, too," said Bertram. "Don't you believe it?"

"Go and eat your slops," said Bertram's mama. But she was interested in what the pig had said about Baby Sam's tooth. So she looked to see if he had really cut a tooth. He had, and that pleased her. But even then she did not believe Bertram's story.

Bertram ate the potato peelings, but he did not like them very much. He slept that night under the porch. The next morning he decided to go over to George Fish's house and get him to find the wand and change him back into himself. George was usually on his front steps at this time, playing with his cat. But he was not there now. Of course! George must have gone to the party. If he had, he would not be back until Monday, and it was only Saturday now. Bertram found some acorns and ate them for his breakfast.

Ginny, after her night in the doghouse, was cold and hungry. She was digging up carrots in the garden and had

125

eaten only one, when her mama came to the back door and shooed her away. Ginny wanted her bath and her orange juice.

Things went on like that over Sunday. But on Monday morning, George was out on his front porch with his cat. As Bertram started to come over, George began throwing stones at him.

"Hi!" said Bertram. "Cheese it!"

George was surprised at hearing a pig talk. Then he said, "Well, I wasn't going to hurt you. I thought you were going to root up our lawn."

"Listen, George," said Bertram, "don't you know who I am? I'm Bertram, and I'm in a fix. I've been changed into a pig."

"Oh, I didn't recognize you at first," said George. "How did it happen?"

Bertram told him.

"That's too bad," said George, "especially as you missed

a perfectly grand party. Well, I'll see if I can find your wand, only I'm not sure I can work it."

So George went over to Bertram's house and asked Bertram's mama if he could come in and look for something. "If it's your cat," she said, "it isn't here."

"But it isn't my cat," said George. "It's something that belongs to Bertram—something he has to have right away."

"Well, he'll be home now any time from the party. Then he can look for it himself."

"But he sent me for it," said George. "He's busy." So Bertram's mama let him in, and it took him only a few minutes to find the magic wand. George picked it up and examined it. Down towards one end there was a tiny dent.

"No wonder it was out of order," thought George. So he smoothed out the dent and went back to where Bertram was waiting. He waved the wand in a sort of circle and said a magic word. And presto! the pig vanished and Bertram stood there in its place.

"Thanks awfully," said Bertram. "Now let's go and find Ginny. She's been changed into a porcupine. I forgot to tell you."

They found her near the doghouse, and Bertram had the thrill of changing her back into herself.

Ginny was none too grateful though, and it was a long time before she quite forgave him. But when Peggy Linder

127

found out why neither of them had come to her party, she gave another one that very week.

As for the two mamas, you can just imagine how they felt when they learned the truth. They were so sorry for the way they had treated their dear children that there was nothing they would not do to make up for it. They took them to the movies and bought them toys and candy bars and balloons. And when they could not think of any other things to give them, they just gave them dimes. And after that they were unusually kind to dumb animals and never drove one from their doors.

WHAT HAPPENED?

Bertram decided to change someone into a tiger. Whatever gave him that idea?

One of Bertram's problems was to get Ginny into the tiger's cage. What success did he have?

Baby Sam spoiled Bertram's plans. How did he spoil them? What did he do to Bertram and Ginny? How did Bertram finally get changed back into a boy again?

THINK IT OVER

Stories that combine fact and fancy are usually funny. Bertram is a real boy. But the magic wand is make-believe. What things happen in the story that could be real? What things happen that are all make-believe?

Many funny things happen in this story. For example, Bertram's mother doesn't seem surprised when a pig talks to her. Why is this funny? What do you think is the funniest thing in the story?

Magicians seem to do many magic tricks. Can you explain how they pull rabbits out of empty hats?

The author did not tell us anything about the scene. Why is the *place* not important in this story?

THE MAD FARMER'S
SONG

My father he left me three acres of land,
Sing ivy, sing ivy;
My father he left me three acres of land,
Sing holly, go whistle, and ivy!

I plowed it all with a ram's horn,
Sing ivy, sing ivy;
And sowed it all over with one peppercorn,
Sing holly, go whistle, and ivy!

I harrowed it with a bramble bush,
Sing ivy, sing ivy;
And reaped it with my little penknife,
Sing holly, go whistle, and ivy!

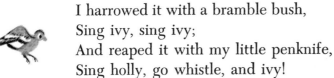

THE ELEPHANT'S CHILD

Rudyard Kipling

In the High and Far-Off Times the Elephant, O Best Beloved, had no trunk. He had only a blackish, bulgy nose, as big as a boot, that he could wriggle about from side to side; but he couldn't pick up things with it. But there was one Elephant—a new Elephant—an Elephant's Child—who was full of 'satiable curtiosity, and that means he asked ever so many questions. *And* he lived in Africa, and he filled all Africa with his 'satiable curtiosities. He asked his tall aunt, the Ostrich, why her tail-feathers grew just so, and his tall aunt, the Ostrich, spanked him with her hard, hard claw. He asked his tall uncle, the Giraffe, what made his skin spotty, and his tall uncle, the Giraffe, spanked him with his hard, hard hoof. And still he was full of 'satiable curtiosity! He asked his broad aunt, the Hippopotamus, why her eyes were red, and his broad aunt, the Hippopotamus, spanked him with her broad, broad hoof; and he asked his hairy uncle, the Baboon, why melons tasted just so, and his hairy uncle, the Baboon, spanked him with his hairy, hairy paw. And *still* he was full of 'satiable curtiosity! He asked questions about everything that he saw, or heard, or felt, or smelt, or touched, and all his uncles and his aunts spanked him. And still he was full of 'satiable curtiosity!

One fine morning in the middle of the Precession of the Equinoxes, this 'satiable Elephant's Child asked a new fine

"The Elephant's Child" from *Just So Stories* by Rudyard Kipling. Copyright, 1902, 1907, by Rudyard Kipling. Reprinted by permission from Doubleday & Company, Mrs. George Bambridge, and The Macmillan Company of Canada, Ltd.

question that he had never asked before. He asked, "What does the Crocodile have for dinner?" Then everybody said, "Hush!" in a loud and dretful tone, and they spanked him immediately and directly, without stopping, for a long time.

By and by, when that was finished, he came upon Kolokolo Bird sitting in the middle of a wait-a-bit thorn bush, and he said, "My father has spanked me, and my mother has spanked me; all my aunts and uncles have spanked me for my 'satiable curtiosity; and *still* I want to know what the Crocodile has for dinner!"

Then Kolokolo Bird said, with a mournful cry, "Go to the banks of the great gray-green, greasy Limpopo River, all set about with fever trees, and find out."

That very next morning, when there was nothing left of the Equinoxes, because the Precession had preceded according to precedent, this 'satiable Elephant's Child took a hundred pounds of bananas (the little short red kind), and a hundred pounds of sugar cane (the long purple kind), and seventeen melons (the greeny-crackly kind), and said to all his dear families, "Good-by. I am going to the great gray-green, greasy Limpopo River, all set about with fever trees, to find out what the Crocodile has for dinner." And they all spanked him once more for luck, though he asked them most politely to stop.

Then he went away, a little warm, but not at all astonished, eating melons, and throwing the rind about, because he could not pick it up.

He went from Graham's Town to Kimberley, and from Kimberley to Khama's Country, and from Khama's Country he went east by north, eating melons all the time, till at

last he came to the banks of the great gray-green, greasy
Limpopo River, all set about with fever trees, precisely as
Kolokolo Bird had said.

Now you must know and understand, O Best Beloved,
that till that very week, and day, and hour, and minute, this
'satiable Elephant's Child had never seen a Crocodile, and
did not know what one was like. It was all his 'satiable
çurtiosity.

The first thing that he found was a Bi-Colored-Python-
Rock-Snake curled round a rock.

" 'Scuse me," said the Elephant's Child most politely,
"but have you seen such a thing as a Crocodile in these
promiscuous parts?"

"*Have* I seen a Crocodile?" said the Bi-Colored-Python-
Rock-Snake, in a voice of dretful scorn. "What will you ask
me next?"

" 'Scuse me," said the Elephant's Child, "but could you
kindly tell me what he has for dinner?"

Then the Bi-Colored-Python-Rock-Snake uncoiled himself very quickly from the rock, and spanked the Elephant's Child with his scalesome, flailsome tail.

"That is odd," said the Elephant's Child, "because my father and my mother, and my uncle and my aunt, not to mention my other aunt, the Hippopotamus, and my other uncle, the Baboon, have all spanked me for my 'satiable curtiosity—and I suppose this is the same thing."

So he said good-by very politely to the Bi-Colored-Python-Rock-Snake, and helped to coil him up on the rock again, and went on, a little warm, but not at all astonished, eating melons, and throwing the rind about, because he could not pick it up, till he trod on what he thought was a log of wood at the very edge of the great gray-green, greasy Limpopo River, all set about with fever trees.

But it was really the Crocodile, O Best Beloved, and the Crocodile winked one eye—like this!

"'Scuse me," said the Elephant's Child most politely, "but

do you happen to have seen a Crocodile in these promiscuous parts?"

Then the Crocodile winked the other eye, and lifted half his tail out of the mud; and the Elephant's Child stepped back most politely, because he did not wish to be spanked again.

"Come hither, Little One," said the Crocodile. "Why do you ask such things?"

" 'Scuse me," said the Elephant's Child most politely, "but my father has spanked me, my mother has spanked me, not to mention my tall aunt, the Ostrich, and my tall uncle, the Giraffe, who can kick ever so hard, as well as my broad aunt, the Hippopotamus, and my hairy uncle, the Baboon, *and* including the Bi-Colored-Python-Rock-Snake, with the scale-some, flailsome tail, just up the bank, who spanks harder than any of them; and *so*, if it's quite all the same to you, I don't want to be spanked any more."

"Come hither, Little One," said the Crocodile, "for I am the Crocodile," and he wept crocodile-tears to show it was quite true.

Then the Elephant's Child grew all breathless, and panted, and kneeled down on the bank and said, "You are the very person I have been looking for all these long days. Will you please tell me what you have for dinner?"

"Come hither, Little One," said the Crocodile, "and I'll whisper."

Then the Elephant's Child put his head down close to the Crocodile's musky, tusky mouth, and the Crocodile caught him by his little nose, which up to that very week, day, hour, and minute, had been no bigger than a boot, though much more useful.

"I think," said the Crocodile—and he said it between his teeth, like this—"I think today I will begin with Elephant's Child!"

At this, O Best Beloved, the Elephant's Child was much annoyed, and he said, speaking through his nose, like this, "Led go! You are hurtig be!"

Then the Bi-Colored-Python-Rock-Snake scuffled down from the bank and said, "My young friend, if you do not now, immediately and instantly, pull as hard as ever you can, it is my opinion that your acquaintance in the large-pattern leather ulster" (and by this he meant the Crocodile) "will jerk you into yonder limpid stream before you can say Jack Robinson."

This is the way Bi-Colored-Python-Rock-Snakes always talk.

Then the Elephant's Child sat back on his little haunches, and pulled, and pulled, and pulled, and his nose began to stretch. And the Crocodile floundered into the water, making it all creamy with great sweeps of his tail, and *he* pulled, and pulled, and pulled.

And the Elephant's Child's nose kept on stretching; and the Elephant's Child spread all his little four legs and pulled, and pulled, and pulled, and his nose kept on stretching; and the Crocodile threshed his tail like an oar, and *he* pulled, and pulled, and pulled, and at each pull the Elephant's Child's nose grew longer and longer—and it hurt him hijjus!

Then the Elephant's Child felt his legs slipping, and he said through his nose, which was now nearly five feet long, "This is too butch for be!"

Then the Bi-Colored-Python-Rock-Snake came down from the bank, and knotted himself in a double-clove-hitch round the Elephant's Child's hind legs, and said, "Rash and inexperienced traveler, we will now seriously devote ourselves to a little high tension, because if we do not, it is my impression that yonder self-propelling man-of-war with the armor-plated upper deck" (and by this, O Best Beloved, he meant the Crocodile), "will permanently vitiate your future career."

That is the way all Bi-Colored-Python-Rock-Snakes always talk.

So he pulled, and the Elephant's Child pulled, and the

Crocodile pulled; but the Elephant's Child and the Bi-Colored-Python-Rock-Snake pulled hardest; and at last the Crocodile let go of the Elephant's Child's nose with a plop that you could hear all up and down the Limpopo.

Then the Elephant's Child sat down most hard and sudden; but first he was careful to say "thank you" to the Bi-Colored-Python-Rock-Snake; and next he was kind to his poor pulled nose, and wrapped it all up in cool banana leaves, and hung it in the great gray-green, greasy Limpopo to cool.

"What are you doing that for?" said the Bi-Colored-Python-Rock-Snake.

" 'Scuse me," said the Elephant's Child, "but my nose is badly out of shape, and I am waiting for it to shrink."

"Then you will have to wait a long time," said the Bi-Colored-Python-Rock-Snake. "Some people do not know what is good for them."

The Elephant's Child sat there for three days waiting for his nose to shrink. But it never grew any shorter, and, besides, it made him squint. For, O Best Beloved, you will see and understand that the Crocodile had pulled it out into a really truly trunk same as all Elephants have today.

At the end of the third day a fly came and stung him on the shoulder, and before he knew what he was doing he lifted up his trunk and hit that fly dead with the end of it.

" 'Vantage number one!" said the Bi-Colored-Python-Rock-Snake. "You couldn't have done that with a mere-smear nose. Try and eat a little now."

Before he thought what he was doing the Elephant's Child put out his trunk and plucked a large bundle of grass, dusted it clean against his forelegs, and stuffed it into his own mouth.

" 'Vantage number two!" said the Bi-Colored-Python-Rock-Snake. "You couldn't have done that with a mere-smear nose. Don't you think the sun is very hot here?"

"It is," said the Elephant's Child, and before he thought what he was doing he schlooped up a schloop of mud from the banks of the great gray-green, greasy Limpopo, and slapped it on his head, where it made a cool schloopy-sloshy mud-cap all trickly behind his ears.

" 'Vantage number three!" said the Bi-Colored-Python-Rock-Snake. "You couldn't have done that with a mere-smear nose. Now how do you feel about being spanked again?"

" 'Scuse me," said the Elephant's Child, "but I should not like it at all."

"How would you like to spank somebody?" said the Bi-Colored-Python-Rock-Snake.

138

"I should like it very much indeed," said the Elephant's Child.

"Well," said the Bi-Colored-Python-Rock-Snake, "you will find that new nose of yours very useful to spank people with."

"Thank you," said the Elephant's Child, "I'll remember that; and now I think I'll go home to all my dear families and try."

So the Elephant's Child went home across Africa frisking and whisking his trunk. When he wanted fruit to eat he pulled fruit down from a tree, instead of waiting for it to fall as he used to do. When he wanted grass he plucked grass up from the ground, instead of going on his knees as he used to do. When the flies bit him he broke off the branch of a tree and used it as a fly-whisk; and he made himself a new, cool, slushy-squshy mud-cap whenever the sun was hot. When he felt lonely walking through Africa he sang to himself down his trunk, and the noise was louder than several brass bands. He went especially out of his way to find a broad Hippopotamus (she was no relation of his), and he spanked her very hard, to make sure that the Bi-Colored-Python-Rock-Snake had spoken the truth about his new trunk. The rest of the time he picked up the melon rinds that he had dropped on his way to the Limpopo—for he was a tidy Pachyderm.

One dark evening he came back to all his dear families, and he coiled up his trunk and said, "How do you do?" They were very glad to see him, and immediately said, "Come here and be spanked for your 'satiable curtiosity."

"Pooh," said the Elephant's Child. "I don't think you people know anything about spanking; but I do, and I'll show you."

Then he uncurled his trunk and knocked two of his dear brothers head over heels.

"Oh, Bananas!" said they, "where did you learn that trick, and what have you done to your nose?"

"I got a new one from the Crocodile on the banks of the great, gray-green, greasy Limpopo River," said the Elephant's Child. "I asked him what he had for dinner, and he gave me this to keep."

"It looks very ugly," said his hairy uncle, the Baboon.

"It does," said the Elephant's Child. "But it's very useful," and he picked up his hairy uncle, the Baboon, by one hairy leg, and hove him into a hornets' nest.

Then that bad Elephant's Child spanked all his dear families for a long time, till they were very warm and greatly astonished. He pulled out his tall Ostrich aunt's tail-feathers; and he caught his tall uncle, the Giraffe, by the hindleg, and dragged him through a thorn-bush; and he shouted at his broad aunt, the Hippopotamus, and blew bubbles into her ear when she was sleeping in the water after meals; but he never let anyone touch Kolokolo Bird.

At last things grew so exciting that his dear families went off one by one in a hurry to the banks of the great gray-green, greasy Limpopo River, all set about with fever trees, to borrow new noses from the Crocodile. When they came back nobody spanked anybody any more; and ever since that day, O Best Beloved, all the Elephants you will ever see, besides all those that you won't, have trunks precisely like the trunk of the 'satiable Elephant's Child.

WHAT HAPPENED?

The Elephant's Child was full of " 'satiable curtiosity." What he is really trying to say is "insatiable curiosity" which means that he is so full of curiosity he can never have all his questions answered.

What were some of the questions the Elephant's Child asked of his relatives? How did they answer him?

Finally someone suggested that the Child should go to the banks of the great gray-green, greasy Limpopo River all set about with fever trees. Who suggested this? What answer was the Elephant's Child supposed to find there?

Two animals helped the Child to get a new nose. Who were they? How did each one help?

The Child found that his new nose was very helpful. What advantages did the new nose have over the old one?

THINK IT OVER

This is a good story to read aloud. In fact, it is meant to be read aloud. Choose a favorite part and practice reading it aloud. Then read it to the class. Or you may want to take turns reading the dialogue as if it were a play.

Kipling, the author, uses many words that make you see a picture as you read. For example, he says the Bi-Colored-Python-Rock-Snake was *curled* around a rock. What are some other expressions that make the story vivid and interesting? What part of the story seems funniest to you?

All young children ask questions. Perhaps you can tell about some time when you became tired of answering the questions of a younger brother or sister. Should you act the way the Elephant's Child's relatives acted when he asked questions of them? Why do you think they were not more polite in answering him?

142

THE BORED GOBLINS

Dorothy Brown Thompson

What do the goblins do
  When it isn't Halloween?
    How do they spend the whole long year
    While no one cares if their ways are queer
    Or if their appearance is weird—oh, dear—
I wouldn't be one—would you?

What do the goblins do
  While they wait for Halloween?
    While the months are tediously creeping by
    And no one in all the world asks why
    There aren't any goblins about—oh, my—
I wouldn't be one—would you?

What do the goblins do
  Until next Halloween?
    When never an incantation comes—
    No "abracadabras" or "fi-fo-fums"
    Do they just sit twirling their goblin thumbs?
I wouldn't be one—would you?

"The Bored Goblins" by Dorothy Brown Thompson. Reprinted by permission of the author.

OWLS TALKING

David McCord

I think that many owls say *Who-o*:
At least the owls that I know do-o.
But somewhere when some owls do not-t,
Perhaps they cry *Which-h, Why-y,* or *What-t.*

Or when they itch-h
They just say *Which-h,*
Or close one eye-e
And say *What-t Why-y.*

"Owls Talking" from *Far and Few* by David McCord, by permission
of Little, Brown and Company.

144

SHUSH SHUSH, THE BIG BUFF BANTY HEN

Carl Sandburg

Shush Shush was a big buff banty hen. She lived in a coop. Sometimes she marched out of the coop and went away and laid eggs. But always she came back to the coop.

And whenever she went to the front door and laid an egg in the doorbell, she rang the bell once for one egg, twice for two eggs, and a dozen rings for a dozen eggs.

"Shush Shush, the Big Buff Banty Hen" from *Rootabaga Stories* by Carl Sandburg. Copyright, 1922, 1923, by Harcourt, Brace and World, Inc.; renewed 1950, 1951, by Carl Sandburg. Reprinted by permission of the publishers.

145

Once Shush Shush went into the house of the Sniggers family and laid an egg in the piano. Another time she climbed up in the clock and laid an egg in the clock. But always she came back to the coop.

One summer morning Shush Shush marched out through the front gate, up to the next corner and the next, till she came to the post office. There she walked into the office of the postmaster and laid an egg in the postmaster's hat.

The postmaster put on his hat, went to the hardware store and bought a keg of nails. He took off his hat and the egg dropped into the keg of nails.

The hardware man picked up the egg, put it in *his* hat, and went out to speak to a policeman. He took off his hat, speaking to the policeman, and the egg dropped on the sidewalk.

The policeman picked up the egg and put it in *his* police hat. The postmaster came past; the policeman took off his police hat and the egg dropped down on the sidewalk.

The postmaster said, "I lost that egg, it is my egg," picked it up, put it in his postmaster's hat, and forgot all about having an egg in his hat.

POST OFFICE

Then the postmaster, a long tall man, came to the door of the post office, a short small door. And the postmaster didn't stoop low, didn't bend under, so he bumped his hat and his head on the top of the doorway. And the egg *broke* and ran down over his face and neck.

And long before that happened, Shush Shush was home

in her coop, standing in the door saying, "It is a big day for me because I laid one of my big buff banty eggs in the post-master's hat."

There Shush Shush stays, living in a coop. Sometimes she marches out of the coop and goes away and lays eggs in pianos, clocks, hats. But she always comes back to the coop.

And whenever she goes to the front door and lays an egg in the doorbell, she rings the bell once for one egg, twice for two eggs, and a dozen rings for a dozen eggs.

THINK IT OVER

"Absurd" means "contrary to reason," or *impossible*. Absurd things are often funny. Name the absurd things in this story which make it funny.

The first two paragraphs and the last two paragraphs in this story are almost exactly alike. Authors often repeat part of a story, usually near the end. Can you think of a reason why they do this?

The author of this story is very famous. He has written books and poems for grownups as well as stories and books for younger readers. What else can you find out about Carl Sandburg's interesting life?

147

THE SHIP OF RIO

Walter de la Mare

There was a ship of Rio
  Sailed out into the blue,
And nine and ninety monkeys
  Were all her jovial crew.
From bo'sun to the cabin boy,
  From quarter to caboose,
There weren't a stitch of calico
  To breech 'em—tight or loose;
From spar to deck, from deck to keel,
  From barnacle to shroud,
There weren't one pair of reach-me-downs
  To all that jabbering crowd.
But wasn't it a gladsome sight,
  When roared the deep-sea gales,
To see them reef her fore and aft,
  A-swinging by their tails!
Oh, wasn't it a gladsome sight,
  When glassy calm did come,
To see them squatting tailor-wise
  Around a keg of rum!
Oh, wasn't it a gladsome sight,
  When in she sailed to land,
To see them all a-scampering skip
  For nuts across the sand!

"The Ship of Rio" from *Collected Poems, 1901-1918*, by Walter de la Mare. Copyright, 1920, by Henry Holt and Co., Inc. Copyright, 1948, by Walter de la Mare. Reprinted by permission of the literary estate of Walter de la Mare and The Society of Authors as their representative.

HANS CLODHOPPER

Hans Christian Andersen

In an old farmhouse in the country lived a man and his
two brilliant sons. The sons were very clever fellows.
They had made up their minds to propose to the king's
daughter. She had said that she would marry the man
who had most to say for himself.

The two brothers took a week to get ready. One of
them knew the Latin dictionary by heart and could say
the town newspapers forward and backward for three
whole years. The other knew all the laws of all the
corporations. He therefore thought he could talk about
all affairs of state.

"I shall certainly win the king's daughter," each
brother thought. Their father gave each son a fine horse.
The one who knew the Latin dictionary by heart had a
coal-black stallion. The one who knew all about law had
a milk-white horse.

Just as the brothers were ready to ride away to see
the princess, the third brother came by. (There really
were three brothers, but no one paid any attention to this
one. He was called Hans Clodhopper and he was not
brilliant like his brothers.)

"Where are you going?" Hans asked.

"To court to ask the hand of the princess in marriage."

"Preserve us then! I must go, too," said Hans Clodhopper.

The brothers laughed and rode away. "Poor stupid Hans!" they said.

"Please give me a horse, Father," Hans asked. "I want to get married to the princess."

"Stuff and nonsense," said his father. "No horse for you. The princess wants a husband who always has something to say. Your brothers are fine fellows. But you have nothing to say."

"Then I'll ride my old billy goat," said Hans Clodhopper. And he seated himself on the billy goat, dug his heels into the animal's sides, and galloped away.

Soon he caught up with his brothers. They were riding very silently for they had to store up every good idea which they wanted to say later on.

"Hello," said Hans. "See what I found along the road," and he showed them a poor dead crow.

"What on earth do you want that for, Clodhopper?"
asked the brothers.

"To give to the king's daughter, of course."

The brothers laughed and rode on. Soon Hans rode
up to them again.

"Hello. See what I found along the road," and he showed
them an old wooden shoe with the top part torn off. "This
is for the princess, too."

The brothers laughed again. "Silly brother," they said.

A third time Hans came riding up on his goat. "Hello,"
he said. "See what I found along the road. Now this is
really famous."

"Why," said the brothers, "that is only sand from the
ditch!"

"Indeed it is," said Hans Clodhopper, "and the very
finest sand, too." And he filled his pockets with it.

151

The two brothers rode ahead and arrived at the castle a whole hour before Hans. At the gate all the suitors were given tickets, in the order of their arrival. There were many handsome men waiting to ask for the hand of the princess. Each in turn went in to see her. And each in turn lost the power of speech as soon as he entered the room.

"No good," said the princess. "Away with him!"

Finally came the turn of the brother who knew the Latin dictionary. But he had entirely forgotten it while he stood waiting. He walked into the princess' room. The floor squeaked and the ceiling was made of looking glass. The brother saw himself standing on his head. At every window sat three secretaries and an alderman. They wrote down on paper all that was said. It was terrible, the brother thought. And so warm! He was very uncomfortable.

"It's terribly hot in here," said the suitor.

"That is because my father is roasting chickens today," said the princess.

There the brother stood like a fool. He had not expected this kind of conversation and he could think of nothing to say, just when he wanted to be especially clever.

"No good," said the princess. "Away with him." And he had to leave.

Then in came the second brother.

"There's a fearful heat here," said he.

"Yes, we are roasting chickens today," said the princess.

"What did you—what?" he stammered, and all the secretaries wrote down, "What did you—what?"

"No good," said the princess. "Away with him."

Then in came poor Hans Clodhopper, riding his billy goat right into the room.

"What a warm fire you have here," he said.

"That is because my father is roasting chickens," said the princess.

"Fine," said Hans. "Then I can get my crow roasted, too," and he pulled the crow from his pocket.

"Of course," said the princess. "But have you anything to roast it in? I have no pots nor pans."

"Ah, but I have. Here is my cooking pan," and Hans brought out the wooden shoe and stuffed the crow into it.

"Very nice indeed," said the princess. "But what shall we baste it with?"

"Oh, I always carry basting in my pocket," said Hans. And he poured a little of the fine sand from his pocket.

The three secretaries and the alderman wrote down every word. But that did not trouble Hans.

"Now I like that," said the princess. "You have an answer for everything. You always have something to say for yourself—just what I want in a man. You shall be my husband. Every word we have said will be in the papers tomorrow, for at every window are three secretaries and an alderman."

So Hans Clodhopper married the princess and became king, even if he couldn't say the dictionary through or talk about the law.

And you can read about it in the alderman's newspaper if you wish.

THINK IT OVER

One brother knew his Latin dictionary by heart and could say the town papers forward and backward for three whole years. This did not make him bright enough to win the princess. Why was his knowledge useless?

Hans' brothers thought he was not very bright. But he won the princess. What things did he pick up along the road to the palace? How did each thing help later on?

Hans won the hand of the princess because he could put what he had to good use. Why is it important to be able to use what you have learned? What other stories or real-life happenings can you tell to show how someone used what he knew wisely?

THE FIRST THANKSGIVING

Aileen Fisher

Out of the woods the Indians came
into the Pilgrim village,
bringing their gifts of nuts and game,
bearing the fruits of tillage.
Out of the shadows and up the banks
Indians came for the feast of thanks.

"When we were hungered," the Pilgrims said,
lifting their eyes to heaven,
"Father, they showed us the way to bread:
water, and meal, and leaven . . . "
The Indians looked to the heavens, too,
not understanding . . . and yet they knew!

"The First Thanksgiving" by Aileen Fisher. Reprinted by permission of the author and *Story Parade*, Inc.

TWO FABLES

Aesop

A hungry wolf put on a sheep's skin and joined a flock of sheep. For many days he could kill and eat sheep whenever he was hungry. Even the shepherd did not know he was a wolf. But one night the shepherd decided to kill one of his own flock for food. He took the wolf and killed him on the spot.

"It does not pay to pretend to be what you are not."

A shepherd boy used to have fun for himself by calling, "Wolf, Wolf!" Then, when the village people ran to help him, he would laugh and tell them it was only a joke. One day a wolf really did come to get the sheep. The shepherd boy called "Wolf, Wolf!" But the villagers thought this was another joke and did not come to help.

"Liars are not believed, even when they tell the truth."

THINK IT OVER

Each of these fables ends with a proverb. A *proverb* is a short, colorful way of saying something true. Often the proverb has to do with conduct, or how people should behave.

Here are three more proverbs. Can you think of any others?

"A merry heart maketh a cheerful countenance."

"Waste not, want not."

"A rolling stone gathers no moss."

Explain what each proverb means. Perhaps your class will want to make up fables to illustrate some other proverbs.

THE MOON'S FIRST CHRISTMAS TREE

Richard E. Drdek

Dan Anderson stretched his legs to relieve cramped muscles. He shifted his weight as much as he could in the narrow hiding place. Moving slowly, he inched backwards toward a bulkhead and a resting place for his back. It was going to be a long trip and, although a stowaway couldn't expect first class accommodations, he might as well be as comfortable as possible.

As he slid backwards, he heard the space ship's captain say to the co-pilot, "Something must be wrong back there." Dan froze in terror. To be caught now would spoil all of his plans.

The captain's voice drifted back to him again. "There's something shifting around in the cargo hold. I no sooner get the ship balanced than it's out of balance again."

"Everything is tied down securely," the co-pilot replied. "I made sure everything was tied down when we loaded up on Moon."

"Something's wrong," the captain insisted. "The controls feel as if we're a hundred pounds overloaded."

"I don't see how that can be," the co-pilot answered. "I checked everything before we left Moon. Not an ounce more than we should have was put on the ship."

"The Moon's First Christmas Tree" by Richard E. Drdek. Used by permission of the author.

"Better check," the captain ordered. "Maybe one of the loading crew left something on board that shouldn't be there."

Dan saw the co-pilot coming down the passageway. He wished he could make himself disappear. He knew he'd have a hard time trying to explain why he was stowing away on the first space ship bound for Venus.

The co-pilot checked each crate of fuel and every box of supplies. He examined the knots in the ropes and tried to rock each box or crate. Slowly he worked his way to the back of the cargo hold where Dan lay hidden. Then he stopped near the crate that concealed Dan, put his hands on his hips, and looked around.

"Maybe he'll go away," Dan thought. He could feel beads of sweat forming on his forehead, and there was a sick feeling grinding at his stomach.

The co-pilot checked more crates, pulled on some more ropes, and found one box of fuel loose. He pulled the rope taut and tied another knot. Having found one of the cases wobbly, the co-pilot renewed his efforts and set himself to the task of securing the entire load in the rear of the hold.

When he first saw Dan, he jumped back in surprise. Then he reached down, took hold of the shoulder straps on Dan's space suit, and lifted him bodily out of the hiding place. With Dan tucked under his arm like a sack of potatoes, he walked forward. He dumped the boy next to the captain.

"Here's the extra weight," he said.

Dan scrambled to his feet and stood at attention. He was more frightened than he had ever been, but he was determined to be a good soldier and not show his fear.

The captain was so surprised on seeing him that he could say nothing but "Who? - - - What? - - - How? - - - "

Dan wasn't without words. "Please take me with you. I've got to go to Venus. Please take me. I promised the kids a Christmas tree. Please take me, won't you?"

The captain wrinkled his forehead into a frown. "What's all this?" he demanded.

"Next week is Christmas, and I have to—*just have to*—

161

get a Christmas tree. We've been living on Moon for five years. Some of the kids have never seen a Christmas tree. I promised them that they would have one this year."

"Why didn't you order one from Earth?" asked the captain.

"I tried that. They said the supply ships were so packed with necessary things that they couldn't find room for a tree. When I heard about this space ship stopping at Moon on the way to Venus, I thought I'd go along and see if I couldn't get a tree there."

The captain and co-pilot looked at Dan with puzzled expressions, as if they didn't quite know what to make of it all.

"There's nothing growing on Moon," Dan went on. "Not a tree, a shrub, or even a blade of grass. There's nothing to make a Christmas tree out of. We've been living in caves, and, gee, a tree would sure make the kids happy."

"Who are you?" the captain asked.

"I'm Dan Anderson."

The captain turned to the co-pilot and said, "I know

him. His father is the chief engineer of that group that went to Moon. They've set up a colony there. With Moon as a supply stop, now we can go on and explore all the other planets."

Turning to Dan, he said, "This is a dangerous trip. No one has ever been to Venus before. We may never come back."

"But everything might turn out all right," Dan said cheerfully. "And I might find a Christmas tree."

"What do we do?" asked the co-pilot. "Should we turn around and take him back to Moon?"

The captain thought a while. He checked his gauges and made some calculations. Then he said, as if he were thinking out loud, "If we turn around and go back, we might not have enough fuel to make the trip. If we go back to Moon, we might as well go back to Earth."

Dan felt terrible. For the first time he realized what he had done. If the ship had to go all the way back to Earth, it would mean another year before they could take off again. Their flight had been planned for a time when Moon would be directly between Earth and Venus and when Venus would be at its nearest point to Earth.

"Don't turn back," Dan said. "Really, I'm not worth it. Too much work has gone into planning this trip. I should have known better. Whatever happens to me will be my own fault."

The captain put his hand on Dan's shoulder, sighed heavily, and said, "That's the way it'll be. Now we'd better call your mother and father and tell them where you are."

Dan brightened considerably. The pilots were not angry with him, and he was on his way to Venus. "You don't have to call my folks," he grinned. "They know where I am; I left a note."

The captain and the co-pilot broke into loud laughter. Here was a boy who was on his way to almost anything, and he was as cheerful as if he were on his way to a Sunday-school picnic. There was no need for anyone to worry—he had left a note!

The captain became serious. "Well, Dan," he said. "We're all in this together. Either the three of us come back, or none of us makes it. We all sink or swim together."

The three adventurers shook hands on that.

"By the way," said the captain, "we might as well know each other's names. I'm Gene Dent and the co-pilot is Lou Carven."

This made Dan feel like a real member of the crew. He sat up front and watched the dials and gauges as if he knew all about them. He could see Venus growing larger

in the front window of the ship. The sun, bright and hot, was off a little bit to the left. Except for the sun, which was like an enormous spotlight, and the glowing Venus, everything was in darkness. Of course there were millions of stars, but they were far off in front, above, below, and behind them. Stars danced all around. It was as if Dan floated in a huge globe pinpricked with thousands of tiny holes which let the light blink through. These were the stars, and they winked and danced on the black velvet lining of the globe. The sun, a brilliant Roman candle, and Venus, a shiny golden reflector, were suspended there with him.

Three and a half days after they had left Moon, Captain Dent said, "Fasten your safety belts. We're going to start slowing up for a landing. I'm putting on reverse power."

Dan braced himself for the jolt. Even then it came suddenly, and he felt as if he were going to break through the chest and leg straps holding him to his seat. He saw the needle on the radio speedometer drop quickly from one hundred times the speed of sound to ten times, five times, and then sound speed. The needle then began showing speeds in hundreds of miles per hour.

The space ship slipped through the twenty-five hundred miles of clouds, which hid the planet from Earth's view, like a train speeding through a tunnel. When they broke through, there stretched before them a green, lush Venus.

"Oh, boy! Trees!" was all that Dan could say.

Captain Dent brought the ship in for a smooth landing on a grassy field.

"Stay close to the ship in case we have to make a quick get-a-way," Captain Dent warned.

As soon as the door was opened, Dan tightened his space helmet and dashed out. He ran directly to the nearest tree. It was about as tall as he was, and all green. It wasn't like anything he had ever seen. It was more like the trees that Dan's science teacher on Earth said grew millions of years before man—the large fern trees that became Earth's coal deposits.

"A tree!" Dan shouted. "I've found a tree!"

Captain Dent and Lieutenant Carven stood by the space ship. Lou had boxes into which he put samples of soil, minerals, and plant life. Captain Dent had instruments which he used to measure oxygen, hydrogen, moisture, and other properties which would make it possible for Earth men to live there.

Dan was on his way back to the ship to get his ax when he saw columns and columns of strange creatures moving toward him. They were green like everything else on the planet, and they were just a little bit bigger than Dan. As they came closer, he could make out arms, legs, and heads.

The creatures had no necks; their heads rested directly on their bodies, and their heads were the widest part of them. To Dan, they looked like walking matches. All carried curious weapons. Their uniforms were a shade darker green than the men themselves. Each had two eyes and a mouth but no nose. And none had hair on his head.

They had come up so suddenly, as if they had sprung from the ground, that Dan and his companions were taken by surprise. Before they could get back into the space ship, they were surrounded, and there were so many of the green creatures that it was useless to try to fight.

"Let's go peacefully," Gene whispered. "We'll try to show them that we mean no harm."

The Venus men closed around in a circle and made Dan, Gene, and Lou march. One, whom Dan thought must be the leader because his uniform was blue instead of green, led the way. The Earth men had to take small steps to keep from walking on the leader's heels. When they finally came to a stop, they were in front of a huge rounded building. It was made of something that looked like glass. Its size and shape were probably designed, Dan thought, to make as much use of natural light and heat as possible.

Most of the Venus men remained outside as the leader

167

marched the three Earth men into the building. They went through a large entrance hall and into a room where a matchstick something sat behind a desk. He was like all the others except that his clothes looked loose fitting and comfortable. Lined along the wall were more soldiers.

When the three stood before the desk, the match-like man said, "Why do you invade us?"

The three Earth men were astonished.

"You speak our language," the captain gasped.

"Of course," said the Venus man. "I speak all the languages of Earth. We have been studying you for some time. We followed your flight from Earth to Moon and to us. Now, I ask again: Why do you come? Is it to make war?"

"I assure you," Gene answered, "we come in peace."

"That is hard to believe," said the Venus man. "If you had meant a peaceful journey, you would have told us that you were coming. You could have asked our permission instead of trying to sneak in."

"We had no idea that we could communicate with you," replied Captain Dent. "If we had known how, we would have asked for landing permission."

"I cannot believe that," their leader said. "If your engineers could make a space ship to land here, they could have found a way to contact us."

He turned to the soldier in blue and said, "Lock these Earth men up. Then destroy their space ship."

"No," Gene begged. "Let us go free so that we may return to Earth and tell our people of peaceful neighbors on your planet."

"I cannot do that," the Venus man said. "You will go back to Earth and tell them of our weakness. Then our clouds will be filled with war ships. We will be destroyed."

"But we mean *peace*," said Gene.

"I wish that I could believe it," the Venus leader said, and he made a motion with his hand that meant them to be taken away and locked up.

Dan broke away from the guard and rushed to the desk. "If we had come for any other reason than peace, would our people have sent a boy?"

Four guards grabbed Dan and began dragging him away. The leader stopped them and waved Dan toward him.

"Why *did* you come?" he asked.

"I came for a Christmas tree," Dan said.

The Venus man looked puzzled. "Will you repeat that?"

"I came for a Christmas tree."

"This I do not understand," said the Venus man.

"I have been living on Moon for five years," Dan explained. "Nothing grows there. There is nothing but rock. We live in caves to protect us from the great heat and terrible cold. There is no beauty on Moon. In four days it will be Christmas. I came here to see if I could get a Christmas tree to take to the children on Moon."

The Venus man looked annoyed. "What is this—this Christmas business?"

Dan told him the story of Christmas and how it was the birthday of the Prince of Peace. He told him how the Christmas tree had come to represent peace, friendship, and good will.

The Venus man looked at him with suspicion. "And what do you do with this tree?"

"We put bright and shiny things on it. Sometimes we put presents on it."

"Presents? What are they?"

Dan tried hard to think of a way to explain a present. Then he thought of the Christmas gift he had received last

169

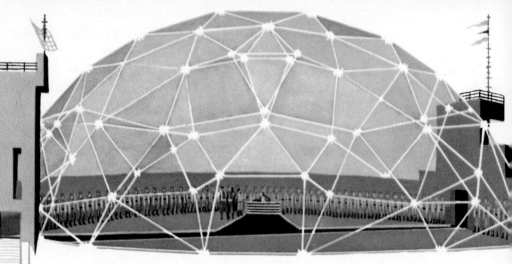

year, a new belt with a gold buckle. He took the belt off and handed it to the Venus man.

"What is that?" asked the man.

"It's yours. I'm giving it to you. It's a present. Merry Christmas."

The Venus man looked at it and then looked at the boy. "Is it mine now?" he asked.

"Of course," Dan replied.

"Why do you give it to me?"

"It's a sign of friendship and good will."

"I like it," said the Venus man. "What can I give you?"

"Nothing."

"But I must Merry Christmas *you*."

"A tree," said Dan.

"You shall have it. Merry Christmas."

The Venus man arose from his desk and faced the men in the room. "Why wasn't I told of this wonderful Christmas thing on Earth?" he demanded. "You call yourselves scientists and you hadn't even learned about their wonderful Christmas. Stupids!"

Without waiting for an answer, he turned and led the way back to the space ship. He had two of his men cut down a tree for Dan and load it into the ship. When they were ready to leave, the Venus man bade them all good-by and asked them to come again.

"Don't forget," he said to Dan. "You must come next Christmas for another tree. Good-by, and Merry Christmas!"

The space ship roared away on full power.

Captain Dent said, "Thanks, Dan. You saved our lives."

Dan grinned from one side of his space helmet to the other. "I got a Christmas tree," he said. "The Moon will have its first Christmas tree!"

WHAT HAPPENED?

Dan was a stowaway. What does this mean? Why did he want to go to Venus? The pilot and co-pilot were worried when they found Dan. Why were they worried? Why couldn't they just take him back to the Moon?

The people on Venus were strange. Describe their appearance. How were they similar to Earth men?

The men of Venus were not glad to see Dan and his friends. Of what were they afraid? How did Dan make them feel friendly? What did he do that lets you know he was unselfish?

THINK IT OVER

Authors who write science-fiction stories try to make them as scientifically accurate as possible. Can you give any evidence to support what the author of this story says about the moon—that there are no trees or shrubs there? Do you know any scientific reasons we have for thinking that Venus may have growing things on it?

What things are happening in science today to prepare for interplanetary travel? What has the world learned since the first rocket reached the Moon?

171

WORDS FROM AN OLD SPANISH CAROL

Ruth Sawyer

Shall I tell you who will come
   to Bethlehem on Christmas Morn,
who will kneel them gently down
   before the Lord, new-born?

One small fish from the river,
   with scales of red, red gold,
one wild bee from the heather,
   one gray lamb from the fold,
one ox from the high pasture,
   one black bull from the herd,
one goatling from the far hills,
   one white, white bird.

And many children—God gave them grace,
bringing tall candles to light Mary's face.

Shall I tell you who will come
   to Bethlehem on Christmas Morn,
who will kneel them gently down
   before the Lord, new-born?

"Words from an Old Spanish Carol" from *The Long Christmas* by Ruth Sawyer. Copyright, 1941, by Ruth Sawyer. Reprinted by permission of The Viking Press, Inc., New York.

UNIT FOUR
Children's Theater

AT THE THEATER

The sun was bright when we went in,
  But night and lights were there,
The walls had golden trimming on
  And plush on every chair.

The people talked; the music played,
  Then it grew black as pitch,
Yes, black as closets full of clothes,
  Or caves, I don't know which.

The curtain rolled itself away,
  It went I don't know where,
But, oh, that country just beyond,
  I do wish we lived there! . . .

And then it's over and they bow
  All edged about with light,
The curtain rattles down and shuts
  Them every one from sight.

It's strange to find the afternoon
  Still bright outside the door,
And all the people hurrying by
  The way they were before!

Rachel Lyman Field

"At the Theater" from *Taxis and Toadstools* by Rachel Field. Copyright 1926 by Doubleday & Company, Inc. Reprinted by permission of the publisher.

PLAYMAKING

FOR EVERYONE

Floy Winks DeLancey

THE FIFTH GRADE
PRESENTS
THEATER-IN-THE-ROUND

"Here's your costume, all ready for the play this evening."

Mother put the brown paper parcel on the table and leaned over to pat down the lock of black hair that always stood straight up on the very top of Joe's head.

"Swell!" Joe gulped down the last sip of chocolate milk, grabbed the bag, and raced for the front door.

"You and Dad be sure to be on time," he shouted as he banged the door behind him. "Remember this is really something special."

The play really was something special Joe thought to himself, as he hurried down Clover Street toward Theodore Roosevelt School. The fifth grade was giving "Puss in Boots." And they were using a new way of presenting their play—a way the teacher called "theater-in-the-round."

"Some people call it arena style," she had told the class when they first started planning. "Instead of using a stage, we'll give the play right in the middle of our own classroom. We'll move all the desks into a circle, and you will act in the middle of the room with your audience seated all around you."

It'll be just like a football stadium, Joe chuckled to himself as he rounded the last corner on his trip. Just like a football stadium, only round instead of oval. And a play instead of a football game, of course!

When Joe reached his room everyone else was there.

"Joe Sewall!" Miss Harris gave a sigh of relief. "We thought you'd never get here. We're using the fourth-grade room for the boys' dressing room. Now climb into your costume quickly. After all, Joe, you're the Cat himself, and the play can't even begin without you."

The costume was a beauty, Joe thought, as he pulled off his T-shirt and blue jeans. Mother had made it from an old gray blanket. It looked something like the pajamas his little sister Anne wore in the winter time, with the feet built in. And Mother had made a beautiful curved tail out of heavy twine. The tail had to be pinned on after Joe was in the costume.

"Here, I'll pin the old thing for you," Rick Smith volunteered. Rick was the King's Footman and he wore a long beard made of string.

"Ouch!" Joe jumped two feet into the air. "You're supposed to pin it on the costume, not *me*." He reached out to pull off Rick's beard, but Rick jumped back just in time. And since Miss Harris came in then, Joe didn't think it was a very good idea to chase after Rick.

Finally the show was ready to begin. The properties for the first scene were already placed in the middle of the fifth-grade classroom, and the mothers and fathers sat all around the room in a circle. Three narrow aisles led to the stage in the center of the room. One entrance was from Miss Harris' office, and the other two aisles led to the hall doors.

Everyone knew his lines; at least everyone thought so.

But the very first thing Tim Gray, who was playing the Miller's Son, made a mistake. Tim was supposed to say, "My father left me nothing but a cat." But somehow the words came out, "My father let me have his hat."

Joe laughed so hard he thought he'd never stop, but he did manage to make his laughs sound like a cat's "Mi-aouw," and all the people in the audience laughed right along with him.

From then on everything went pretty well. At the end of the first scene the actors just walked off the stage and up the aisles between the rows of seats. Then the stage crew rearranged the stage to make it look like the Ogre's palace.

The play was really good. The fifth-graders had planned all the conversation themselves, with Miss Harris' help. The Cat (that was Joe, of course) promised the Miller's Son he

would make him rich. The Cat took the rabbit to the King, met the Princess, and finally killed the Ogre, who had turned into a mouse by then. Unfortunately, when the Cat was killing the Ogre, the Ogre stepped on the Cat's tail and pulled it off. But by that time Joe felt so much at home on the stage that he didn't even care. He just picked up the tail, flipping it around in his hand like a lasso. And the audience laughed again as if this were the very best part of the show.

When the play was over, the actors all walked to the center of the stage and bowed —first to one side of the room and then, in turn, to the other three sides, so that the audience could see them all, face to face.

Miss Harris had ice cream and cake for the cast, and the parents waited outside in the corridor until the children were through eating.

Joe was still wearing the Cat suit when he met his father and mother in the hall.

"You were just fine," Mother said proudly. "I like this theater-in-the-round kind of play. I felt just as if I were right on the stage with you."

Dad gave Joe a man's handshake and said, "Nice work, Son."

"It was fun," Joe said. "I hope we have another play real soon—another arena one, I mean." He wound the cat's tail around his arm like a snake and took a few cat jumps down the steps. "Next time we're going to do a science-fiction story. Wish I could wear a space suit that would really work. I could sail all the way to Mars."

Mother laughed. "Right now you're sailing all the way home to bed," she said. And the three of them hurried off toward Clover Street.

PANTOMIME FUN

Remember that pantomime includes both action and facial expression. When you act out the following suggestions make your face show *how* you feel. Your entire body can show expression, too. Would your shoulders sag if you were happy? Would you be moving briskly if you were sad?

Pantomimes for One

1. someone old and unhappy
2. someone angry
3. a man shoveling a heavy load
4. someone excited
5. a woman taking clothes in out of the rain
6. a farmer fighting a swarm of bees

Pantomimes for Two

1. a father teaching his son to shoot a bow and arrow
2. a person teaching a friend to ski
3. two Indians paddling a canoe
4. two children roller skating together
5. a general giving a medal to a brave soldier

You and the person acting with you may want to plan an incident around your act. Try pantomiming something else that might happen in each of the ideas above.

Group Pantomimes

Divide your class into groups. Have each group act in pantomime one of the incidents described here.

Before you begin the pantomime, suggest words which might describe each character and have them written on the board. If you are pretending to be a policeman in the first pantomime, you must think and feel like a policeman. What words (adjectives) describe a policeman? Thinking about words like "kind," "honest," "stern," will help you get into the mood of the pantomime.

1. A policeman walking his beat meets: (*a*) a housewife coming home from the grocery, (*b*) a small girl playing hopscotch, (*c*) a mischievous boy with a sling shot. Will the policeman's facial expression be the same when he meets each person?

2. A school nurse examines in her office: (*a*) a child with a possible contagious disease, (*b*) a boy who is only pretending to be sick, (*c*) a child with a broken arm.

3. A group watches a World Series game on television. Part of the group is rooting for one team, part for another. Each character's mood will change with the score.

4. A photographer takes a group picture of a kind mother, a hurried father, a vain sister, a clumsy brother, and a wriggly baby.

5. Hikers reach the top of a steep hill, build a fire, and prepare their supper.

PLAYMAKING WITH WORDS

Here is a famous story and a scenario from which you can make a play. A *scenario* describes the action in a play but does not contain the complete dialogue.

MOSES

Exodus i:1—ii:22

The Pharaoh, or ruler, of the Egyptians did not like the Israelites who were living in his country. He was afraid they would soon become greater in number and in power than his own people. Because of this fear, he gave orders that all boy babies born to the Israelites should be killed.

A baby boy was born to Jochebed and Amram, Israelite parents. His mother kept him hidden for several months so that the soldiers of the Pharaoh could not find him. When he grew older she thought of a plan which might save the child's life. Jochebed made a little box like a boat and covered it with pitch, to make it waterproof.

Then she placed the baby in the box. She and Miriam, the baby's twelve-year-old sister, put the box in the river where the Pharaoh's daughter came each day. Miriam hid nearby to watch.

The mother then returned home.

The Pharaoh's daughter with her maids came to the river bank. Soon she saw the box floating among the reeds. When she found the baby inside, the Princess knew at once that this must be one of the Hebrew children.

"It would be cruel to let such a beautiful baby as this die," she said. Just then Miriam, as if by accident, came running from her hiding place.

181

"What a pretty baby!" Miriam said. "Shall I find a Hebrew woman to be nurse to the child for you, and take care of it?"

"Do that," said the Princess. "Go, child, and find a nurse for the baby. I shall call him Moses, for that word means 'drawn out,' and he has been drawn out of the river."

Quickly Miriam ran and brought the baby's own mother to the Princess. Jochebed cared for Moses in her own home until he was no longer a baby. Then he went to live in the palace of the Princess.

And so little Moses was saved. Although he grew up among the Egyptians, he loved his own people. And when he became a man, Moses lived among the Hebrews and became their leader.

Scenario for "Moses"

CHARACTERS: Jochebed; Miriam; the Princess; three maids; soldiers of the Pharaoh

COSTUMES: Toga-like robes

SCENE ONE: The home of Jochebed and Amram. Furnishings—table, chairs, wood box

SCENE TWO: The river bank—a mural painting of water and bulrushes could serve as a backdrop. If you act the play in arena style no set will be needed.

SCENE ONE

Miriam and her mother are on stage when the play begins. The mother is walking back and forth crying; Miriam is playing with the baby. They talk about the new law that all boy babies of the Hebrews are to be killed.

Suddenly they hear the sound of footsteps.

"Quick!" cries Miriam. "It is the soldiers coming to search for boy babies. We must hide my brother."

They hide the baby in the wood box and cover him with clothes.

The soldiers enter and search but do not find the baby. After they leave, the mother sits by the table and cries. Miriam tries to soothe her. Then the mother thinks of a plan to save the baby. She and Miriam discuss the plan, then leave with the baby in the wood box.

SCENE TWO

The Pharaoh's daughter and her handmaidens can be heard laughing and talking off stage. Miriam hurries in with the baby and hides him in the rushes. Then she hides on another part of the stage. The Pharaoh's daughter and her friends enter. They talk and laugh until they hear a baby cry.

"What is that?" asks the Pharaoh's daughter. The maidens search and find the child. They all admire him.

"I shall keep the baby for my own," says the Princess.

Miriam runs from her hiding place. "What a pretty baby!" she says. "Would you like me to find a nurse for the baby?"

The Princess agrees. Miriam leaves. While she is gone, the Princess continues to admire the baby.

Miriam returns with her mother. The Pharaoh's daughter and her maids leave after making plans for Jochebed to care for Moses. Miriam and her mother talk about how happy they are; then they, too, leave the stage.

183

A STORY TO MAKE
INTO A PLAY

Try this story first in pantomime. Then add conversation to make it a real play.

ANDROCLES AND THE LION

TIME: 100 A.D.

PLACE: Scene One—Africa. Scene Two—The Arena in Rome.

COSTUMES: Aluminum foil armor for Roman soldiers; a simple toga for Androcles; lion's mane and tail for the Lion.

Androcles was a runaway slave hiding in an African forest. One day, near the path on which he walked, he saw a Lion moaning with pain. Androcles started to run away. But, when he saw that the Lion was not chasing him, Androcles turned back to see what was wrong.

The Lion held out a bloody paw.

"Poor fellow," said Androcles kindly. "You have a thorn in your foot. Hold still now, old fellow, and out it will come! Be brave now!" Androcles pulled out the thorn. Then he tore a strip from his shirt and bandaged the wound.

"You'll be all right now, my friend," he said.

Some time later both the Lion and Androcles were captured by the Emperor's men and taken across the sea to Rome. There, because he had run away, Androcles was sentenced to battle barehanded with a wild animal. This was what the people of that ancient time called "great sport."

All Rome gathered to see the sport. The poor slave was dragged into the arena. Then the soldiers lifted the door of the wild-animal cage and out walked a huge lion. Madly the animal dashed toward poor Androcles, who was cowering in one corner. Suddenly the animal stopped and sniffed. Then he jumped up and down, wagging his tail like a friendly pup. Androcles peeped out from behind his hands and recognized his old friend.

Androcles and the Lion rushed together, hugging one another. Then they danced together around the arena. The Emperor could not believe what he saw. He hurried into the arena—keeping at a safe distance from the Lion, of course!

"What strange power have you, slave?" he asked. "Why are the wild beasts of the forest your friends?"

Then Androcles told him the story of how he had met the Lion long before and pulled a thorn from his paw.

"Thus is kindness rewarded with kindness," said the Emperor thoughtfully. "You are a free man from this time on, Androcles. You and your Lion shall go free together."

Planning the Play

Make a scenario for the story about Androcles. This is a good play to act in theater-in-the-round style.

One group of pupils may write the scenario, deciding on (*a*) the number of scenes and (*b*) the conversation.

One group may make plans for the staging, deciding on (*a*) the properties for each scene and (*b*) the stage arrangement.

A third group may plan the costumes. Where could you find out what kind of clothing people wore in the days of ancient Rome?

After you have written the scenario and planned the play,

186

act it several times so that different pupils may have a chance to perform.

Evaluating a Play

Have several different casts act out the play. While they are acting, notice whether or not any changes should be made in the dialogue or stage directions. Then discuss which cast would be best for your play.

This is called "evaluating" a play. Here are some questions to ask when you evaluate.

1. Did each speech have some part in telling the story?

2. Did each actor pronounce all his words correctly and clearly?

3. Did each character have good facial expression as he said his lines?

4. Was there enough *action* in the play, or did the characters just stand around and talk?

5. Did all the characters work together to make the play interesting? Did any one character try to take the center of the stage too often?

A PLAY
IN THREE EPISODES

Here is a play about Robin Hood. This is your opportunity to enter the great forest of Sherwood and make Robin and his bold band come to life. You will enjoy using the colorful speech of a long ago time as you act out their adventures.

IN SHERWOOD FOREST

Dramatization by Floy Winks DeLancey

CHARACTERS

Robin Hood	Will Scarlet	Much, the Miller's Son
Maid Marian	Alan-a-Dale	Others attending Robin
Little John	Ellen	and Marian
Will Stuteley	King Richard	King's Courtier

TIME: Reign of Richard I PLACE: Sherwood Forest, England SCENES: Stane Lea in Sherwood. Scenes one and three have the same setting—a forest glen. Scene two requires a stream with a rude bridge across it. The stream can be made of crinkled cellophane or waxed paper; a board may be used to represent the bridge.

PROLOGUE

In this our spacious isle, I think there is not one,
But he of Robin Hood has heard, and Little John.
And to the end of time the tales shall ne'er be done
Of Scarlet, George-a-Green, and Much, the Miller's son;
Of Tuck, the merry friar, which many a sermon made
In praise of Robin Hood, his outlaws, and their trade.

(from ROBIN HOOD, *by Michael Drayton)*

SCENE ONE

*Much and Will Scarlet are seated on a log, left center.
Much is out of breath.*

SCARLET. You've made enemies of the King's foresters
now, Much. You will never be able to live outside the
forest again.

MUCH. I care not. Life outside Sherwood is not pleasant
for a Saxon these days. I would I knew who the strong
lad was who forced the foresters to free me this day.

SCARLET. What became of him when you made your
escape?

MUCH. I know not. His arrows flew like magic until the
foresters released me. I ran and called to him to follow.
But I have not seen him since.

SCARLET. Pray God they did not capture him! There
must be others in Sherwood like us, Much. The Norman
lords are cruel masters. There must be others hiding if
we could but find them.

MUCH. Aye, plenty, no doubt.

(*Enter Robin Hood and Will Stuteley. Much and Scarlet start to hide; then they see who has come. They draw to one side. Robin and Will do not see them.*)

STUTELEY. Safe we are here, friend. This is Stane Lea. Foresters never enter this part of Sherwood.

ROBIN HOOD. And many thanks to you, sir, for bringing me here. I fear those foresters might have caught me had you not showed me the secret path. I am Robin Fitzooth, sir, at your service—sometimes called Robin Hood.

STUTELEY (*shaking hands with him*). My name is Will Stuteley, sir. 'Twas a bonnie sight to see your arrows fall into the forester band.

MUCH (*steps forward as Robin and Will reach for their bows*). Stuteley, I have seen this young Robin Hood in action, too. 'Twas to save me he raised his bow today. The foresters were taking me to the Sheriff when a voice cried out, 'Stay there! Free the man!' And arrows came piling into the band—just missing each forester by a hair's breadth. They let me go, and the archer disappeared. I thank you, Robin Hood. (*He shakes Robin's hand.*) I am Much, the Miller's son, Robin Hood—a poor Saxon.

ROBIN (*bows*). This sounds very like a round robin, sir. Earlier this day, Will Stuteley here cut the thongs that held me after the foresters thought to take me to Nottingham. Had he not freed me then, I could not have saved you later.

190

SCARLET (*steps forward*). What were they taking you for, sir?

ROBIN. I was on my way to Nottingham when I found myself in an archery contest with a band of King's foresters. I shot a deer they pointed out to me. Then they seized me as a criminal for killing royal property. Our good friend Stuteley here cut loose my bonds. And here we are.

SCARLET. Your head will pay for that deer, methinks, if they find you.

ROBIN (*laughing*). They won't find me. In sooth, I shall be happy to live always here in the greenwood with friends like you around.

MUCH. And I with you, sir. I owe my life to you.

STUTELEY. You are an outlaw, Robin, from this time on. There is no free life for a Saxon in England now.

ROBIN. Better an outlaw with my head on my shoulders than headless on the Sheriff's platform at Nottingham! (*He laughs.*)

MUCH. Have you no family, sir?

ROBIN. My parents are dead. I have no family.

SCARLET. And no sweetheart? A fine young lad like you?

ROBIN. There was a girl, the Lady Marian Fitzwalter. At Malaset she lives, with broad acres around a castle and deer roaming the glens.

STUTELEY. Your sweetheart, Robin?

ROBIN. Her father, Sir Richard Fitzwalter, has promised

191

that she shall marry a duke. It grieved my heart to leave her.

MUCH. Shall we bring her to the greenwood for you, sir?

SCARLET. There's an outlaw friar near who can perform marriages.

STUTELEY. Say the word, sir. Malaset is not too far.

ROBIN. I shall send word to her where I am. Perhaps some day—(*He pauses.*) But enough of that. If only King Richard were on the throne and not that evil John.

MUCH. Aye, a sad day it was for England when Richard was taken prisoner overseas.

(*All shake their heads in sorrow.*)

ROBIN. Shall we band together, men, and live a merry life in Sherwood? At least until our Richard of the Lion Heart returns?

MUCH. Aye, indeed, sir. And Robin Hood himself shall be our leader. Robin Hood, who wields the mightiest longbow ever seen in Sherwood.

(*All shout approval.*)

SCARLET. There will be other men to join us, sir.

ROBIN. Then listen, my friends. E'en though we be outlaws, we must have laws to follow. What say you to this? We shall wage war only against the Norman tyrants who have taken land and wealth unjustly from our Saxon neighbors. We shall live on the King's deer in the forest, but never shall we kill for the love of killing.

STUTELEY. Aye, sir. Not even a rabbit shall we touch unless we need food.

ROBIN (*pulling a black arrow from the quiver at his waist*). The black arrow shall be our sign. We shall plunder from the wealthy and send a ransom for our King.

ALL. Aye, aye. (*They gather in a circle and clasp hands all together.*)

MUCH. Ho for our brave leader, Robin Hood, prince of archers and from this day on the prince of outlaws.

(*All shout "Hurrah for Robin Hood" as the scene ends.*)

SCENE TWO

Two years later in a meadow in Sherwood. There is a stream with a bridge across it. Enter from right Robin Hood, Stuteley, and Scarlet. The men carry longbows. Robin sits down on a rock near one end of the bridge. The other men stand.

ROBIN. What ho, my men! A dreary day indeed in Sherwood. We've had no sport now for many a day.

STUTELEY. Living with Robin Hood's band is sport enough for us, eh, Scarlet?

SCARLET. Aye, yes. You're not yourself today, Robin. You've been so happy since the Lady Marian came to the forest to be your wife. Can it be then that you tire of greenwood life?

193

ROBIN.   Nay, I'll never tire of greenwood life, nor of Maid Marian, either.   But our life has been dull of late, I'll be bound.   And I worry about King Richard.
(*Enter from left, Marian, Ellen, Maids, and several of Robin's men.   They are on opposite side of bridge from Robin.*)

ROBIN (*rises and takes a step toward his end of the bridge*).   Welcome, Marian and all.   Take care how you cross that flimsy log.   Narrow it is, and the water beneath it wet.
(*He holds out his hand to Marian.   She crosses carefully, taking hold of his hand as soon as she can reach it.   Some of the others cross behind her; some stay on opposite side.*)

ALAN-A-DALE.   Aye, wet enough.   I wouldn't care for a plunge.

ROBIN.   Sit down here by my side, Marian.   A dreary day this has been until you came.

MARIAN.   Life is never dreary in Sherwood.   I have been telling Ellen how it happened that I came to Sherwood Forest, Robin.

ROBIN.   More happiness there has been in our greenwood since you left Malaset to marry me, Marian. 'Twas more than I ever hoped for.

ELLEN.   It must have taken courage, Marian, to travel here alone from Malaset.

MUCH.   Not really alone, Ellen.   One of our men was near at hand every step of the way to protect her if she needed us.   Though she never knew we were near.   And she had no trouble.

ALAN-A-DALE.   But it's trouble we've been giving the world ever since we came to Sherwood, sir.
(*All laugh and agree.*)

SCARLET.   And the Sheriff—we've planned trouble enough for him.

ROBIN.   Aye, the past has been gay enough.   But 'tis the future we must think of.   Many a month has passed since we sent our share of ransom for King Richard and not a word comes from him.

ELLEN.   They said in town before I came here, Robin, that the King would be back soon.

MARIAN. Be of good cheer, Robin. John cannot keep the throne forever.

ROBIN. That I know, Marian. But sadness is upon me this day. Methinks I shall go abroad alone to look for sport, else I'll turn into an old man before my time.

MARIAN. Not alone, sir! The forest swarms with the Sheriff's men!

ROBIN. Aye, alone. But fear not. If I fall into any peril from which I cannot escape alone, I shall blow a loud blast on my horn. (*As he speaks, Robin pats the horn which hangs at his waist.*) And you shall all come to my aid. Away, my friends. (*He turns to Marian.*) Mayhap I'll bring a juicy deer for tomorrow's feast. Farewell, friends. (*He waves them away.*)

(*All exit right; those on left cross bridge and follow others off stage. The men talk among themselves as they leave; Alan and Ellen walk together. Marian turns to wave to Robin. When all are gone, Robin sits down again on the rock and yawns and stretches. He drops his head into his hands. Little John enters, left, on opposite side of stream. He carries a staff which hits against a rock and makes a noise. Robin jumps to his feet.*)

ROBIN (*grabbing his longbow and starting to put an arrow to it*). What do you here? This is Stane Lea in Sherwood Forest. You trespass, sir!

LITTLE JOHN (*angrily*). What now! Since when does Sherwood Forest belong to any one man? A fine fellow you are, to draw your longbow when I have but a staff with which to defend myself. (*He holds up his staff.*)

ROBIN (*throwing down his bow*). That is just, in truth. I will lay by my bow and find me a staff to try if you are stronger than I.

(*He searches among the trees and returns with a stout staff. The two men look at one another across the bridge, then each takes a step forward.*)

ROBIN. Now we are matched. So let us play upon this bridge. The one who falls into the stream shall lose the victory to the other.

LITTLE JOHN. So be it. And I shall not be first to give out. Be sure of that.

(*They parry blows with their staves. Back and forth across the bridge they fight. At last Robin loses his footing and falls into the stream.*)

LITTLE JOHN. Ho! Ho! And where are you now, I pray thee, my good fellow? (*He leans on his staff and laughs.*) (*Robin picks himself from the stream and shakes the water from his face and clothes.*)

ROBIN (*as he climbs to the far bank of the stream*). Truly thou art strong. Our battle is at an end, and I must admit you have won the day. (*He takes his horn and blows a blast.*)

(*Almost immediately his men come running from all sides. Marian and Ellen follow fearfully.*)

STUTELEY. What's wrong, master? You are wet to the skin.

ROBIN. Nothing is wrong, Stuteley. The lad on the bridge there tumbled me into the water. 'Tis an unexpected bath I've had this day.

(*All men begin to move toward stranger, muttering "We'll get him," etc.*)

ROBIN. Halt, men! That is a stout fellow there. (*He turns to Little John.*) My men will not harm you, friend. These are my own foresters, my bowmen. If you will be one of us, you shall soon have a suit of Lincoln green and a bow fit for a man. What say you?

LITTLE JOHN. Here's my hand on it. (*He crosses the bridge and holds out his hand. He and Robin shake hands.*) You must be bold Robin Hood. May I be a true man to you. My name is John Little.

SCARLET (*laughing*). John Little, eh? John LITTLE, you say? (*He measures Little John's height with an upraised arm.*)

STUTELEY. We'll call you Little John.

(*The men crowd around, shouting, "Little John, Little John!"*)

MUCH. Where come you from, sir?

LITTLE JOHN. London.

ROBIN. Any word of the King? Has he been ransomed?

LITTLE JOHN. Richard has returned and John has been set down from the throne.

(*Men shout, women clap hands and talk happily.*)

ROBIN. May God bless our King! (*All bow heads.*) Tomorrow I shall go to Nottingham to the church and there give thanks that the Lion Heart is no longer a prisoner abroad. But now we must prepare a feast for our new man, Little John.

SCENE THREE

Same as Scene 1. Enter King Richard and a Courtier, dressed in bright clothing.

RICHARD. We've hunted Sherwood for a fortnight and no trace of Robin Hood or his men have we seen. I'll be bound he has vanished from the face of the earth just as he vanished from Nottingham dungeon last month when I sent the papers to have him brought to me in London.

COURTIER. My lord, Robin Hood will never bring his bowmen against your armored men. No doubt he thinks we are enemies. I doubt not every step we have made in Sherwood has been watched.

RICHARD Then how will we ever find him? Methinks I need to see this famous outlaw who sent money from his robbing to ransom me out of foreign prison.

COURTIER. Should you disguise yourself as a fat abbot, sire, I trow Robin Hood would appear in a hurry.

RICHARD. A capital idea, that. I think he is no common criminal, this Robin. It must have been a wrong against him that sent him first to hide in the forest. Come, let us find a disguise.

(They exit left. Enter Robin Hood and Marian from right.)

MARIAN. 'Tis good to have you back again in the forest, Robin. When we heard here that the Sheriff had seized you when you went to Nottingham to worship, such sadness in Sherwood was never seen.

ROBIN. Aye, and I'm back all hale and hearty, thanks to King Richard of the Lion Heart. And to Little John, who carried the letter from His Majesty back to the Sheriff.

MARIAN. Tell me again, Robin, what was it the letter said?

ROBIN. That I should be brought to the King in London. And then at night while the Sheriff slept to rest for the journey, Little John and Much freed me from the dungeon and here we are, safe again.

(*Enter King disguised as an abbot. Robin puts Marian behind him and steps forward.*)

ROBIN. Sir Abbot, no man is permitted to travel this part of Sherwood. You must stay with me and my men for a while.

(*He bows low to Abbot; then blows horn; men enter from both sides.*)

KING. And who is it who bars my way?

ROBIN. We are yeomen of the forest who live in the greenwood and take care of the poor. Give us of your plenty for charity's sake, Abbot.

KING. But I have little money, sir. I have just come from the court of the King. Money disappears there in a hurry, let me tell you.

ROBIN. Are you a faithful follower of Richard?

KING. Aye, that I am. I love him as well as I love myself.

(*The men cheer, calling "Richard! Long live Richard!"*)

ROBIN. Then save half your money for the King, sir. We will be content with only half—little as you say you have.

MUCH. We would never take everything a man had, Abbot, if that man followed Richard.

ALAN-A-DALE. But when King Richard was in prison, we took all we could get to help ransom him, of that you may be sure.

KING. You are very kindly outlaws, sir. (*Turning to Robin.*) I trust that you are the Robin Hood I have heard of in the town. My errand here in Sherwood is to bring you before the King. He wants mightily to meet you since you failed to keep the appointment with him in London.

MUCH (*laughing*). We didn't like the escort the King had planned for Robin, Abbot. The fat old Sheriff of Nottingham is no favored traveling companion of ours.

LITTLE JOHN. Aye, we fooled the King and the Sheriff both that day, Abbot. But truly, 'twas only that we needed Robin Hood here more than London needed him.

KING. You do your leader proud, men. I have always heard that Robin Hood was a disloyal fellow who never obeyed Richard's laws.

(*All men shout "No! No!" Some draw their bows.*)

MARIAN (*stepping forward toward the Abbot*). My sire is a just man and loyal, Abbot.

ROBIN. And I love no man in the world so well as the mighty Richard.

KING (*draws cowl from his face and holds up finger with King's ring*). Happy am I to hear that, Robin my lad.

ROBIN. The King! It is the King! Kneel, men, and do honor to Richard.

(*Men kneel on one knee. Marian and women curtsy.*)

KING. Why kneel to me, Robin? Are you not king of the greenwood? Rise. You are a man after my own heart.

(*Robin rises. Other men remain on one knee until he motions for them to rise.*)

You must leave this outlaw world and be my knight.

ROBIN. That will I do gladly, King. I am your man from this day forth.

KING (*turning to Marian, who curtsies again*). And you, my dear, are the daughter of my good old friend, Sir Richard Fitzwalter. Since his death you have become a ward of mine. You gave up much to live in the green-wood. But I must agree you chose a brave man and a bold one for your husband.

ROBIN. The Lady Marian gave up Malaset and all of its acres for me, sire. 'Twas a great sacrifice for her.

MARIAN. No sacrifice, Robin. Life in Sherwood with you and your band has been far happier for me than life at Malaset without you.

KING. Then shall she have Malaset back again. Kneel, Robin. (*Robin kneels.*) I hereby give thee the rank of a noble. (*He touches Robin's shoulder.*) From this day forward you shall be called Earl of Huntingdon. And you, Lady Marian, (*He turns to her.*) shall live with Robin at Malaset. (*He turns back to Robin and his men.*) And all of you, men of Sherwood, shall henceforth be known as bowmen for King Richard of the Lion Heart.

(*Cheers!*)

CURTAIN

EPILOGUE (*Choral Reading*)

On the fairest time of June
You may go, with sun or moon,
Or the seven stars to light you,
Or the polar ray to right you.
But you never may behold
Little John, or Robin bold.
So it is: yet let us sing,
Honor to the old bow string!
Honor to the bugle horn!
Honor to the woods unshorn!
Honor to the Lincoln green!
Honor to the archer keen!
Honor to tight Little John,
And the horse he rode upon!
Honor to bold Robin Hood,
Sleeping in the underwood!
Honor to Maid Marian,
And to all the Sherwood clan!
(*from* ROBIN HOOD, *by John Keats*)

POEMS TO SPEAK TOGETHER

The following poems are fun to say aloud in unison. After you have read each poem a few times, you may want to try a different arrangement of voices. The second poem is a spooky one about shadows and Bogie men. Try to make your voices sound scary as you read.

FREIGHT BOATS

James S. Tippett

Three Boys:	Boats that carry sugar And tobacco from Havana;
Three Girls:	Boats that carry coconuts And coffee from Brazil;
Three Boys:	Boats that carry cotton From the city of Savannah;
All:	Boats that carry anything From any place you will.
Three Girls:	Boats like boxes loaded down With tons of sand and gravel;
Three Boys:	Boats with blocks of granite For a building on a hill;
All:	Boats that measure many thousand Lonesome miles of travel As they carry anything From any place you will.

"Freight Boats" from *I Go A-Traveling* by James S. Tippett. Copyright, 1929, Harper & Brothers. Copyright, 1957, James S. Tippett. Reprinted by permission of Harper & Row, Publishers.

SHADOW MARCH

Robert Louis Stevenson

Boys:
All around the house is the jet-black night;
   It stares through the window pane;
It crawls in the corners, hiding from the
     light,
   And it moves with the moving flame.

Girls:
Now my little heart goes a-beating like a
     drum,
   With the breath of Bogie in my hair,
And all round the candle the crooked
     shadows come,
   And go marching along up the stair.

Three children: The shadow of the balusters, the shadow of
   one saying   the lamp,
   each phrase   The shadow of the child that goes to bed—
All: All the wicked shadows coming, tramp,
     tramp, tramp,
   With the black night overhead.

PLAYING A POEM

Here is a good poem for playmaking. You will want to have one pupil asleep on the stage, dreaming. Other pupils may pantomime the strange dreams. You may also need to use your dictionaries to find out what a "necromancer" is.

DREAMS

Marchette Chute

Once I was a pirate,
A savage, slashing pirate;
I flew the skull and crossbones,
   and I stamped upon the deck.

Once I was a camel,
(A handsome sort of camel)
And ambled in a caravan
   with jewels around my neck.

Once I was a dancer,
And once a necromancer;
I even was a Viking
   with a helmet on my head.

I might have been a carrot
Or a strange Brazilian parrot
If someone hadn't wakened me
   and pulled me
             out
                of
                  bed.

"Dreams" by Marchette Chute. Reprinted by permission of the author and *Child Life*.

A POEM TO MAKE
INTO A PLAY

Although a poem may not really tell a story, it is sure to have ideas that can be used in playmaking. All you need is a little imagination. What ideas for playmaking can you find in the following poem?

A PIPER

Seumas O'Sullivan

A piper in the streets today
Set up, and tuned, and started to play.
And away, away, away on the tide
Of his music we started; on every side
Doors and windows were opened wide,
And men left down their work and came,
And women with petticoats colored like flame,
And little bare feet that were blue with cold,
Went dancing back to the age of gold,
And all the world went gay, went gay,
For half an hour in the street today.

Here are some suggestions for a play from this poem.

1. Several unhappy villagers meet on a street and talk about their troubles. Everyone is sad and discontented.

2. A wandering musician appears. He begins to pipe a tune. Before long, one by one, the unhappy people begin to dance and sing. More people enter as they hear the music. Finally all are dancing and singing.

"A Piper" by Seumas O'Sullivan from *Collected Poems* and reprinted by permission of the author.

3. When the piper stops his music, the villagers thank him. They talk about how much happier they feel, and they sing this song.

THE GALWAY PIPER

Lively

IRISH FOLK SONG

Ev - ry per - son in the na - tion
When the wed - ding bells are ring - ing

Or of great or hum - ble sta - tion holds in high - est
His the breath to lead the sing - ing. Then in jigs the

es - ti - ma - tion Pip - ing Tim of Gal - way.
folks go swing-ing. What a splen - did pip - er.

Loud - ly he can play or low. He can move you
He will blow from eve till morn, count - ing sleep a

fast or slow, touch your hearts or stir your toe,
thing of scorn. Old is he but not out-worn.

Pip - ing Tim of Gal - way!
Know you such a pip - er?

"The Galway Piper" from *The Silver Book of Songs*, published by Hall and McCreary Company.

UNIT FIVE
History Makers

LINCOLN LEARNING

The hearthfire cast a flickering light,
But there was more to learn that night.
A glowing log broke with a snap;
The book was opened to a map;
The boy was learning of a world
Beyond his cabin, here unfurled.
Before his eyes were countries,
And people; now he read of these.
He read and as he read he stored
A fund of knowledge; bright flames roared
Beside him lying on the floor.
These youthful days would form the core
Of manhood wisely, nobly spent—
Emancipator, President.

Louise Darcy

"Lincoln Learning" by Louise Darcy. Reprinted by permission of The Christian Science Monitor.

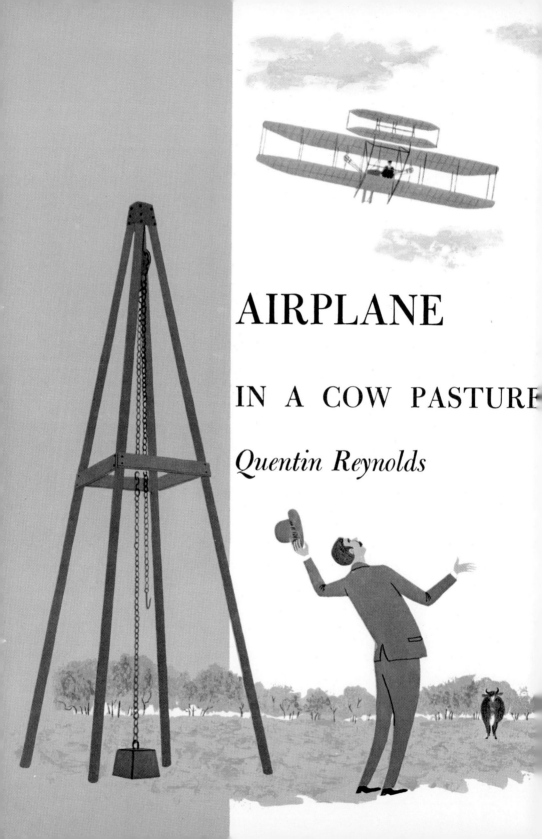

AIRPLANE

IN A COW PASTURE

Quentin Reynolds

Wilbur and Orville Wright made the first successful airplane flight at Kitty Hawk, North Carolina, in 1903. In spite of this the people in their own home town refused to believe that the brothers could really fly.

Torrence Huffman, president of a Dayton bank, owned an eighty-acre cow pasture outside of town. Will and Orv asked him if they could use the cow pasture.

"Somebody said you two have been experimenting with flying machines." Mr. Huffman smiled. "Is that right?"

"That's right," Wilbur said.

"Go ahead, boys, use the field," Mr. Huffman said, "but don't kill any of my cows."

The brothers had decided to build a brand-new flying machine with a sixteen-horsepower engine. They worked hard at it and now, embittered by the attitude of their neighbors, they seldom saw anyone but Charley Taylor and their sister Kate. When they walked along the street, people winked at each other as if to say, "They're the ones who said they flew." Will and Orv ignored the winks and the scorn, but it hurt them to know that their own neighbors thought they had lied.

Mr. Chanute knew they hadn't lied. He went to Paris and made a speech about the flight at Kitty Hawk, and everyone in France became excited about the flying machine

"Airplane in a Cow Pasture" from *The Wright Brothers: Pioneers of American Aviation* by Quentin Reynolds. Reprinted by permission of Random House, Inc. Copyright, 1950, by Random House, Inc.

the Wright brothers had built. They were famous in France, and then in Germany and England, but not in Dayton.

"Why don't they stick to their bicycle shop?" the people said, but the two brothers went right on working. They brought their new flying machine to the cow pasture. But they tried it out only early in the morning. Nobody was going to have a chance to laugh at them. Their new flying machine stayed up longer than the Kitty Hawk machine.

Then one day Wilbur actually circled the field. The new machine could steer. Miracles were happening at this cow pasture every day, but no one saw them except a few cows down at the far end of the pasture. A few days later Orv circled the field three times—a distance of three miles.

One day Will and Orv asked their father and Kate to go to the cow pasture with them.

"Be sure and bring your watch, Father," Will said.

Kate and Bishop Wright stood beside the flying machine.

"I want you to time this flight," Wilbur said. "I've filled the gasoline tank. Now, Orv, take her up."

Orv took her up. The flying machine almost disappeared in the distance, and then it turned and came back. Orv flew over his father's head and waved to him. Then he made a large circle around the field. Bishop Wright kept one eye on his watch. The minutes passed. Fifteen . . . twenty . . . thirty.

"He's been up there half an hour, Will!" Bishop Wright said excitedly.

Finally the flying machine swooped to a gentle landing.

"Thirty-nine minutes!" Bishop Wright gasped.

"I only came down because I ran out of gasoline," Orv explained.

"We can stay up almost as long as we want," Wilbur said. "But we wanted you to see our airplane actually in action."

"Airplane? That's a good name for it," the Bishop said.

Bishop Wright told a few people what he had seen at the cow pasture. They believed him, and now they were willing to believe Wilbur and Orville. People hurried to the bicycle shop to congratulate them, but the two brothers were too busy to see them.

"Where were they when we came back from Kitty Hawk?" Will asked bitterly.

"Well, we've gotten along without them all these years," Orv said. "We can still get along without them."

One day two important men arrived in Dayton. One was French; the other was English. Each wanted to buy the Wright brothers' airplane. Each wanted to pay a huge sum for the exclusive rights to it so that only his country could make it.

"The Germans will make war on us one day," the Frenchman said excitedly, "and with this flying machine we can beat them easily. We can fly over their armies and drop dynamite on them."

"We, too, fear Germany," the Englishman said, "and we are willing to pay you anything you want for the right to make your airplane."

213

"But we are Americans," Wilbur said. "If we gave the airplane to anyone it would be to our own army."

"But Monsieur Wright, if you will forgive me," the Frenchman said, "your own army has already refused it. Your own army is not interested."

Wilbur was startled. It is true that he and Orv had written to the army authorities in Washington, and that the army hadn't been interested. But neither he nor Orv had told anybody about this.

"Nevertheless," Wilbur said now, "we are Americans, and someday perhaps our army will be interested."

The two polite gentlemen from abroad bowed, looked regretful, and left.

"I guess we'd better give a real demonstration," Will said. "I don't blame our army authorities for not being enthusiastic. They've never seen our plane fly."

"All right, Will, we'll give them something to think about," Orv said.

Theodore Roosevelt was President of the United States then. Although he is remembered as a man of action, he was a great reader, and one day he picked up a copy of the *Scientific American*. There was an article in it about the Wright brothers and their flying machine.

214

"Get hold of these two young men," President Roosevelt told his Secretary of War, "and have them give an exhibition. Maybe they have something in that flying machine."

One day a dignified colonel arrived in Dayton. He went to see the Wright brothers. Would they be so good as to honor a request by the President of the United States?

"Frankly, gentlemen," the colonel said, "we in the army don't think the flying machine has any future, but the President has ordered us to get in touch with you. Will you give a demonstration of your machine?"

"You bet we will," Orville said, and Wilbur nodded vigorously.

"Of course we will see that it is held in secret," the colonel said, smiling.

"Why?" Wilbur asked.

"Well, in case things go wrong . . . I mean if it doesn't get off the ground . . ." The colonel faltered. "We don't want you gentlemen to be humiliated."

"Don't worry about us, Colonel," and Orv laughed. "Ask a thousand, ask a million people to the demonstration. We don't care."

A huge crowd assembled at Fort Meyer, Virginia, the place the army had picked out for the test. The Secretary of War

was there. A dozen generals were present and at least fifty reporters. Nobody really believed that the queer-looking machine could actually fly. Did it fly? Orville took it up and circled the field for one hour. When he landed, the crowd went wild with enthusiasm. Even generals with three stars on their shoulders swarmed all over the two calm, unexcited brothers.

"I'd give anything to ride with you in that flying machine," a young lieutenant said. Orville looked at him. The young soldier's eyes were shining. He was Lieutenant Fred Lahm.

"Well, come on, Lieutenant," Orville said. "Climb up in back of me and hang on. . . . Clear the crowd away, please."

The crowd fell back. Orv took off easily with the Lieutenant hanging on. They circled the field three times and then landed. The crowd was almost hysterical. It had seen a miracle happen. The generals were thoughtful.

This airplane could carry a 180-pound passenger in addition to its pilot. That meant it could carry a 180-pound bomb. Perhaps it could carry more than one bomb.

"Have you sold the rights to this plane to any foreign government?" a general asked.

"We're Americans, General," Orv said simply. The general shook his hand and said, "Will you have time to see the Secretary of War tomorrow?" The two brothers nodded.

The next morning they woke up to find themselves famous. Every newspaper in the country had headlines about their flight. They were the most famous men in the world now. There were big crowds outside the War Department building when they went to see the Secretary of War.

"You've done a great thing, young men," the Secretary of War said, shaking hands with them. "The first men in history to fly. Tell me, can you build larger airplanes than the one you showed us yesterday?"

"It's just a matter of power," Orville said. "If we make stronger, more powerful engines, we can fly bigger airplanes."

"If the power is there we can make a kitchen table fly," Wilbur said.

"I'm sure you can," the Secretary said. "We want you to build airplanes for our army. Will you?"

"Of course we will," Orv said, and Wilbur added, a bit embarrassed, "I hate to mention it, Mr. Secretary, but . . . we have no money. We spent our last cent to finish the plane we showed you yesterday."

"You'll never need money again." The Secretary smiled. "We'll advance all the money you need. Can you build an airplane that will go forty miles an hour?"

"You name the speed you want," Orv said. "We'll build it to your specifications."

"May we make them in Dayton?" Will said. "That's our home town."

"Of course you may," the Secretary of War said. "When are you planning to return?"

"On the midnight train," Will told him.

"That'll give you time to accept a dinner invitation," the Secretary said, smiling. "The President of the United States

has asked me to extend an invitation to dinner tonight. Can you make it?"

Wilbur looked at Orville. Orville looked at Wilbur.

Orville winked at Wilbur. "I think we can make it," he said gravely.

And then the two boys who had learned to fly walked out of the office, arm in arm.

WHAT HAPPENED?

Why wouldn't the Wright brothers sell their airplane plans to the French or the English?

A United States president was one of the first Americans to become interested in the new flying machine. Who was he? What did he do to help the Wright brothers?

Tell what the United States Army thought at first about the importance of this new flying machine. Then tell how the Army changed its mind.

THINK IT OVER

The people in Dayton laughed at the Wright brothers for their silly ideas. You remember that people laughed at Columbus when he said the world was round. Why is it sometimes hard for people to accept new ideas?

Name some of the things we have today which your grandparents never dreamed of when they were your age. Perhaps you can discuss this with your grandparents.

Men have dreamed of flying for hundreds of years. One of the earliest to write about experiments in flying was an artist. His name was Leonardo da Vinci and he lived about five hundred years ago. Men have also dreamed for a long time of visiting other planets. Do you think such a dream can ever come true?

219

SOLO AT SEA

Adele de Leeuw

Amelia Earhart was the first woman to fly the Atlantic as a passenger. In this story she is planning to fly the Atlantic as pilot. Her husband, George Putnam, called by everyone GP, and Bernt Balchen, her co-pilot on other trips, are helping her to ready the plane.

Soon Bernt Balchen was at Teterboro Airport in New Jersey, working on Amelia's plane. It was not new. It had been on long air voyages, and it had to be made stronger. Extra fuel tanks must be installed in the wings to carry the heavy load of gasoline. The cabin must be cleared so that still another tank could be put in. And room must be made for more instruments, and a drift indicator, and three compasses. Amelia believed in being really prepared.

April came and went, and so did half of May. At last the plane was ready. Every day now, Amelia and her husband and Bernt and her mechanic, Eddie Gorski, waited for weather reports. "Doc" Kimball of the U.S. Weather Bureau in New York was preparing them for her, as he had on her other flights.

"No one has said a word to him about where you plan

"Solo at Sea" reprinted by arrangement with Grosset & Dunlap, Inc., New York, N. Y., publishers of *The Story of Amelia Earhart* by Adele de Leeuw. Copyright, 1955, by Adele de Leeuw.

to go," GP reported, "but I think he knows what's afoot. Whenever I stop in there he has a twinkle in his eye. Oh, he knows all right, but he's keeping it a secret, too."

Amelia was impatient to start on the first leg of the trip, to Harbor Grace in Newfoundland. Bernt and Eddie were going with her that far. But there was no use starting until Doc Kimball gave the word that everything was right along the way.

How hard it was to wait! It was hard on her husband and her family, too. They watched her anxiously, hoping she might change her mind. It was so long a flight, and such a dangerous one! No woman had done it before.

"Are you sure you want to do this?" GP asked her, more than once. She looked so young and slight. Would she be able to stand such a difficult trip?

"Yes," she answered always. "I want to do this more than anything."

On the twentieth of May, GP went again to Doc Kimball's office.

"The weather looks pretty good today," Doc Kimball said. He pointed things out on his weather maps, explained about the reports he had received from ships on the Atlantic.

"I'll telephone Amelia," GP said. He knew how much this would mean to her, but his heart was heavy, as he telephoned the airport at Teterboro.

"Doc says the weather's good at sea," he told his wife.

Amelia's voice had an excited tone. "And the visibility between New York and Harbor Grace?"

"Fine all the way," GP reported.

Amelia thought a moment. She looked at her watch.

"I'll drive home and get my things and be back here for the start by three o'clock," she said.

"I'll meet you at the airport," GP promised.

Amelia told Bernt and Eddie about the phone call. "I'll be ready to leave by three," she said. "Will you?"

They looked at her admiringly. "We'll be ready," they promised. "It will be a relief to go!"

"That's the way I feel," Amelia laughed.

She drove to her home in Rye to gather up her belongings. She had planned carefully what she would take along. It must be kept simple and as light as possible. There were her flying suit, her maps, a comb, a toothbrush, and a can of tomato juice. That was all.

While she changed into jodhpurs and a silk shirt and windbreaker, she looked out her bedroom window. The soft May air was stirring the cloud of white blossoms on the dogwood tree. The grass was a bright, fresh green, and near the garden wall the flowers that she had planted were showing color. She loved this home where she had been so happy! She stood a moment, very quietly, taking it all in, so that she could remember it.

Would she come back to it? She must!

She ran downstairs and out of the door to her car. No one in the household knew where she was going. She drove rapidly back to Teterboro. When she reached there it was five minutes to three, and her husband was waiting for her.

Amelia said good-by to him, and took her place on the floor of the plane between the gas tanks. Bernt and Eddie climbed in, and Bernt took the controls. Twenty minutes after she had reached the flying field, she and the two men were in the air on their way to St. John's, in Newfoundland. There they spent the night. Next afternoon they were at Harbor Grace.

When they got to Harbor Grace, Amelia went off to the hotel and fell asleep almost at once. She needed all the sleep she could get, so that she could stay wide awake and alert once she was alone. Bernt and Eddie tuned up the ship. Then they sent a message to her. "Ready."

Amelia came down to the lobby almost at once. The desk clerk handed her a telegram. She opened it, saw that it was from her husband, and read it, slowly, with a happy little smile.

Out on the field the plane was waiting. Amelia buttoned

the collar of her flying suit, adjusted her helmet, and tucked in her wind-blown hair. Her eyes were clear and unafraid when she looked at the two men who stood beside the plane.

"Thanks, Bernt, for all you've done. And you, too, Eddie."

They shook her hand. Bernt said huskily, "O.K. So long. Good luck." And Eddie echoed, "Good luck!"

Amelia climbed in, opened up the motors, and was off.

It was just twelve minutes after seven when she pointed the nose of her ship out to sea. There was a long, slow sunset, and the weather was calm. The motors hummed in unison. The moon came up and spread a silver sheen on the water, and turned the clouds to silver.

It was so beautiful! Amelia felt that she had never been so happy. She was doing what she wanted to do—"for the fun of it." She was off on another great adventure. What more could anyone ask of life?

Then she looked at her altimeter which should show her how far she was above the earth. But the hands on the dial were swinging back and forth! The altimeter was broken!

Now she would not be able to tell how high or how low she was flying.

It grew dark. The moon was lost behind a bank of clouds. Almost at once a storm blew up. Thunder rolled. Lightning split the sky in jagged streaks. The plane shook with the violence of the storm, so that she had a hard time keeping it under control. If she could climb above the storm, where the air might be calm—

She climbed and climbed. But then her wings seemed heavy and she looked out to find that ice had formed on them. There was slush on the windowpane. The plane was so heavy with ice it went into a spin, dropping in an almost straight line three thousand feet.

Amelia managed to level off just before hitting the water. She drew a long breath. "Well," she thought, "at least I saved myself that time."

In the lower air the ice began to melt, and the plane could lift again. But the whitecaps on the sea were very close. Amelia tried not to look at them or think about them. She thought only of keeping her plane in position, and hoping that the weather would clear.

In the darkness she suddenly saw a little tongue of flame dart up from the engine. It flickered and wavered, but did not die. She knew what had happened, and how serious it was. The manifold ring had broken where it had been welded together. All she could hope was that the metal was heavy enough so that the manifold ring would last till she landed.

"Even if I turned back to Harbor Grace," she thought, "I still couldn't land in the dark." She decided to take the chance and keep going.

Those were long, anxious hours. When dawn came, the flame did not seem so bright—but it was still there. The clouds formed a bank so heavy that it was like flying over a snow field. Amelia put on dark glasses. But the sunlight on the clouds was still so brilliant that she came down "to fly in the shade" beneath them.

She was not hungry, but she was thirsty. She punctured the can of tomato juice. While she sipped the juice through a straw she noticed again how badly the metal was vibrating. She turned on her reserve tank of gasoline—and discovered that the gauge was leaking.

"I should really come down somewhere—soon," Amelia told herself. "This settles it."

It was hard to tell where she was, because of the masses of clouds. And she could not know how high she was, or how far down she should come, with her altimeter out of order. There was a strong wind blowing. It looked as if another storm were on the way.

She had passed only one ship on her way over the water, near Harbor Grace. She had blinked her lights, but there was no answer, and she felt sure no one aboard had seen her. Now she saw another lone ship. Perhaps that meant she was near land! She should be near the middle of the coast of Ireland, if her course were true.

In a short while the Irish coastline *was* visible, though the hills were almost lost in the low clouds of a thunderstorm. She tried to find a railroad line to follow, but there was

none. She looked for an airfield, but could not find it. The flame was burning more brightly now! The engine was shaking! The gas tank leaking!

The soft green of broad pastures came into view. Cattle grazed contentedly on them. Amelia circled once or twice to find the best place to land, hoping not to disturb them. She flew low, and lower. She skimmed over the meadow, the grass looking brighter green, the cows as large as life, and set her plane down.

It was thirteen hours and thirty minutes since her take-off.

The early morning was peaceful and cool. Amelia slumped a little in her seat in the cockpit. Her long, slender hands lay idle in her lap.

A man came running across the pasture, his eyes wide, his mouth open in astonishment.

Amelia leaned out and said, "I've come from America."

He panted. "Do ye be tellin' me that now?"

Amelia laughed. She knew how he must be feeling. She felt pretty much the same way.

Was it true? The feeling of excitement was so strong it wiped out all her tiredness. It *was* true. She, Amelia Earhart, was the first woman in the world who had ever flown across the Atlantic alone!

WHAT HAPPENED?

Amelia's plane was not new. Many things had to be done to it before she could try her flight across the Atlantic. What were some of these things?

Something on the airplane broke soon after Amelia left Harbor Grace. What was it, and why did its loss make her trip more dangerous?

Later on something else on her plane broke. This, too, was serious. What happened as a result of this break?

Amelia could not find an airport when she reached Ireland. Where did she finally land?

THINK IT OVER

Amelia Earhart was a courageous woman. Many people are courageous even though they do not have a chance to show bravery the way Amelia did. Your parents and friends, and you yourself, are often courageous in small ways. Sometimes it is harder to be brave about little things than about big ones. Can you think of a time when your parents, or someone you know, were courageous?

You may want to read about the rest of Amelia Earhart's life and how she disappeared while trying to fly around the world. How can you find what other books have been written about Amelia Earhart?

When a story makes you wonder how it will turn out it has suspense. What is the suspense in this story? The author gives you some good atmosphere, or feeling for the surroundings, when she describes flying over the sea. What are some of the words that give you a good picture of the storm at sea?

It took Amelia thirteen hours and thirty minutes to fly to Ireland. How does this compare with records set by jet planes today?

HUNTERS AND TRAPPERS

James Daugherty

Daniel Boone in his coonskin cap
Guided movers through Cumberland Gap.
A new-born hope glowed in their eyes
To find a pioneer's paradise.
"Barking" squirrels was Dan's delight.
He killed a big bear in a fight
And cut on a tree in letters square
"HERE'S WHERE D. BOON CILLED A BAR."

Three long-eared hounds went on a spree
And chased a panther up a tree.
When Daniel Boone came up the hill
The yellow panther had a chill.
When Dan'l aimed his gun at him
He climbed way out upon a limb,
And hollered with a fearsome frown,
"Don't shoot, Daniel, I'll come down!"

"Hunters and Trappers" from *The Wild, Wild West*, copyright, 1948, by James Daugherty.
Reprinted by permission of David McKay Company, Inc.

WASHINGTON

Nancy Byrd Turner

He played by the river when he was young,
He raced with rabbits along the hills,
He fished for minnows, and climbed and swung,
And hooted back at the whippoorwills.
Strong and slender and tall he grew—
And then, one morning, the bugles blew.

Over the hills the summons came,
Over the river's shining rim.
He said that the bugles called his name,
He knew that his country needed him,
And he answered, "Coming!" and marched away
For many a night and many a day.

Perhaps when the marches were hot and long
He'd think of the river flowing by
Or, camping under the winter sky,
Would hear the whippoorwill's far-off song.
Boy and soldier in peace or strife,
He loved America all his life!

"Washington" by Nancy Byrd Turner. From *Child Life*, copyright, 1930. Reprinted by permission of the author.

MAJOR GEORGE WASHINGTON

Genevieve Foster

Young Major George Washington, now over six feet tall, and dressed in the blue uniform of a Virginia soldier, stood before the Governor, in his mansion or "Palace" at Williamsburg.

"How soon can you start?" asked the Governor, as he signed, sealed, and handed a letter to George.

"Today, sir," answered George. Soon he was out in the crisp October morning, far down the road on his galloping horse, leaving Williamsburg behind.

It was October 30, 1753. George was twenty-one years old. He was proud to be trusted with this difficult errand. He had asked for it. And he was determined to succeed— though it meant following a dim, uncertain trail into the dangerous Northwest.

The letter which he carried was to be delivered to the commander of a French fort somewhere near the Ohio River. The Governor could not say exactly where. He only knew that the French had come down from the north and were on land that belonged to the English—on the very land, in fact, which the King had given to the Ohio Company. For George, *that* had real meaning. His brother Lawrence had been president of that company of Virginians when they received the land. Before Lawrence died, the Ohio Com-

"Major George Washington," originally titled "The French and Indian War," from *George Washington* by Genevieve Foster. Copyright, 1949, by Genevieve Foster. Used by permission of the publishers, Charles Scribner's Sons.

pany had been planning to build a fort on their land, to protect it from the French. The fort had not been built. The French were there.

Now George was to carry the Governor's firm but courteous letter asking the French commander to leave. How many soldiers he had, how many forts the French had built, how many Indian tribes they had to help them—that, also, George was to find out.

As he rode along, he was thinking over what he needed —arms, ammunition, compasses, tents, food for the horses, presents for the Indians, as well as guides and interpreters. Stopping at Fredericksburg to say good-by to his mother, he found and hired a man who said he could speak French.

Losing no time, they set out for the Blue Ridge Mountains and, in ten days, were as far into the woods as George had ever gone. From there on, he needed a guide. At a small settlement he found a very shrewd one, Christopher Gist, and hired four woodsmen, two of whom spoke the Indian languages. With these guides, they set out for the village of Half King, a famous Indian chief, on the Ohio River. On the way, they learned that three Indian tribes had gone over to the French. What about Half King, was the question. Would they find him friendly or not?

Before finding out, they came to a point, not far from the Indian village, where two rivers joined to form the Ohio. George looked it over most carefully. On this point of land (where the city of Pittsburgh would be in years to come), was where the Ohio Company of Virginia planned to build their fort.

Half King was full of anger at the Frenchmen. This land, he said, was *his*. Frenchmen told him it was *theirs*. That was a bad lie. This was NO white man's land. This was *Indian* land!

George listened gravely, picked his words cautiously, and waited—waited until Half King and three of his braves saw fit to guide them to the French fort.

They trailed after the Indians four days. Then they came upon a log trading post, flying the beautiful white flag of the French, with its golden lilies. A man half French, half Indian, was in charge. The fort, he said, was fifty miles farther on. But, he added, if the Englishman think the Frenchman would leave these lands, he is mistaken. Non! It belong to them. All these Ohio—all these Mississippi valley. LaSalle, a Frenchman discover it, many years ago. So would his commander tell them!

The French commander received Le Major Washeentong at his fort in a perfect manner. He took the Governor's courteous letter, asking him to leave, and wrote an equally courteous letter, saying NO.

Taking that letter back was one long struggle against the bitter cold. For now it was December. The ground was covered with snow. The horses were exhausted. In order to go faster, Washington (now in a suit of buckskin) proposed that he and Gist strap what they needed to their backs and trudge on ahead. Twice they came close to death. Trying to cross a half frozen river, George was hurled from their raft of logs and nearly drowned. Both were shot at by an Indian guide. But they plodded on.

And on January 16th, to the Governor's surprise and delight, Washington was back in Williamsburg. He had a report of the Ohio country, a drawing of the French fort, and the French commander's letter.

In the spring, on his second trip to the Ohio country, Washington was less successful. This time, upon the Governor's order, he took a company of soldiers, not a letter. During the past months, the Virginians had begun, at last, to build their fort at that point of land near the village of Half King. But even before the bright, new logs were all in place, the French had captured the fort. Now they had to be driven out!

Halfway there, in a Great Meadow, surrounded by hills, Washington pitched his camp. He also built a temporary fort, though that low, open meadow was a foolish place to choose. But George had no training as a soldier. He had to learn from his mistakes.

One rainy night in May, an Indian runner came speeding into camp with a message from Half King.

"Frenchmen nearby," said the Indian. "Half King see foot tracks. Thirty Frenchmen—maybe more."

Spies! thought Washington. The French were planning a surprise attack! There was no time to lose. He took forty men. All night they followed the Indian through the rain-soaked woods. Half King joined them. About sunrise, the Indian stopped and pointed. There in a hollow were the Frenchmen!

An order was given to fire. For the first time, Washington heard bullets go whistling past his ears as the Frenchmen sprang to their guns. But too late. Their leader and ten of the men were dead. The other twenty were captured. Washington was overjoyed.

The first battle of his life had been a victory!

But his joy did not last long. On the third of July, five hundred furious Frenchmen, with many Indian allies, came to attack him and avenge the "murder" of their comrades. Those men, they said, were only carrying a message to the English governor.

It was a rainy, dismal day—the day of the battle. Inside his poor, little, unprotected fort in the Great Meadow, Washington had less than half as many men and had been deserted by Half King and his Indians. Not wishing to be captured in that white man's fort, Half King went to watch the battle from the hills.

Washington's men held out as long and bravely as they could, but by nightfall, he was obliged to surrender. In the light of a candle flickering in the wind, his translator read the French paper given him to sign. It said that he must give back the French prisoners and not return to that territory for another year. Washington signed it grimly. Next day, he was allowed to march his soldiers out of the fort with the honors of war, but he went home to Virginia, all his joy blotted out by this defeat.

To add to his misery, he fell ill and lay in bed for long, gloomy weeks at Mount Vernon.

Meanwhile, copies of the paper he had signed reached England, and the King concluded it was time to send soldiers to America to settle what seemed to be turning into war against the French and Indians.

By the following summer, General Braddock had arrived from England, and was in command. Washington, serving under him, was on another trip to recapture the log fort on the Ohio. Too ill, at times, to sit on a horse, he lay on his back in a baggage wagon. Bumping along, he kept fretting over the time wasted by the English general.

General Braddock was an old, experienced commander, but he and his well-trained soldiers had fought their battles in Europe, never in the wilderness. They had never heard wild Indian war whoops, nor known how a stealthy Indian crept up on a foe.

A first, horrible lesson came one day in July. In their brilliant scarlet coats, they were marching along through a narrow road in the forest, not far from the fort. Suddenly they heard a wild yell and bullets whizzing from all directions. Soon they were falling dead and wounded. Yet they saw no enemy! Panic and frenzy swept their broken ranks. Into that stampede of men rode General Braddock on a rearing horse, swinging his sword, shouting, trying to control his frantic soldiers. Washington, too, though still dizzy with fever, rode into the thick of the danger. Bullets whizzed by, pierced his sleeves, killed his horse. He mounted another. Wheeling here and there, he rallied his Virginians.

But the day was lost. General Braddock, himself, was wounded. Washington helped carry him from the field in a litter made of his scarlet sash. A few days later, they buried him there in the road, where his grave would be

hidden from Indian scalp hunters under the tracks of his returning baggage wagons.

Two years later, in 1758, Washington made one last trip with the English soldiers to the Ohio fort. At their approach, the French hastily set fire to the fort and left. So Washington saw it go up at last in crackling flames, that little log fort in the wilderness that had started the French and Indian War.

The French were to lose all of their forts and land in North America by the time the war was over. Washington was to take no further part in it, but he had made a name for himself. At a meeting in Williamsburg, the chairman called attention to him.

"I wish to compliment our Virginia hero," said he, "for his brave and steady behavior from the first warlike actions of the French and their Indians to the capture of their fort."

Washington tried to reply, but no words came.

"Sit down, Mr. Washington," said the speaker, to relieve him. "Your modesty is equal to your bravery, and that exceeds the power of any language I possess."

WHAT HAPPENED?

The first trip George Washington made into the Ohio country was to carry a letter to the French commander. What else was he to do on this trip? What did he bring back with him for the Governor at Williamsburg?

This trip was not the only one Washington made to the Ohio country. How many other trips did he make? What was the reason for each trip?

Half King was angry at the French. Why was he angry? Did he make a good friend for Washington?

THINK IT OVER

In this story, George Washington is fighting on the side of the British. How can you explain this?

General Braddock did not know how to fight an Indian war. Tell some of the things he did that were wrong.

Washington made some mistakes, too. Even our greatest men are not always right. What do you think he learned from this experience which helped him in the Revolutionary War? When you make a mistake, what should you do?

Countries sometimes fight on the same side and then fight against one another later on. It's probably the same way in your gang. Sometimes you are close friends with one person, and then something happens to change your feelings. Perhaps you have heard someone say, "When you are angry, count to ten before you speak." Why is this a good idea? How do you think it might help to save a friendship?

THE YOUNG COLUMBUS

Nancy Byrd Turner

The little son of the weaver went up and
    down the room,
Two paces out, two paces back, to the
    drone of the driving loom.
His hands were deft with the shuttle,
    but his fancy wandered free—
He was full of an old, old wonder: *What
    lies beyond the sea?*

In the open door of the cottage he saw
    a picture framed,
The sweep of the waters wide and blue
    when the western skyline flamed,
With a golden pathway shining when the
    sun was very low.
He shaded his eyes to watch it: *Where
    does the bright way go?*

Down on the wharves at evening he marked
    the turning tide,
The long waves pulling outward slow, the
    water surging wide,
Forever drawn to the distance, and rest-
    less evermore.
He sat and mused in the twilight: *What
    of that other shore?*

"The Young Columbus" by Nancy Byrd Turner. Reprinted by permission of the author.

The little son of the weaver wove on,
  the long years through,
And, watching still and wondering still,
  to manhood's stature grew;
He traced with trembling finger dry
  scroll and map and chart.
What lies beyond the sea? he said, the
  old dream in his heart.

The long tides swung to seaward, the
  wind drew to the west;
He gathered ships for his going, because
  he could not rest.
The white sails filled and fluttered;
  the old shores dimmed behind;
He set his course unflinching for the
  goal that he must find.

America, my country! the years are very
  long,
But still we lift our praise today,
  and still we sing our song
For him, the weaver's little son, who
  questioned wistfully:
*What's over the other side?   What lies
  beyond the sea?*

241

WHAT HAPPENED?

This poem tells the story of Columbus from boyhood to manhood. As a boy Columbus had to work hard. What did he do? What did he think about as he worked? What did he do in the evenings after work?

Columbus had a dream. What was it? Did the dream ever come true?

THINK IT OVER

Some people think it is hard to tell what a poem is about. But it is usually easy. In a very few words you can tell about "The Young Columbus." You might begin this way: "When Columbus was a boy he dreamed about what was beyond the sea." How would you finish telling the meaning of the poem? Tell in your own words what the last stanza says.

Have you ever heard the words "day dreaming"? Perhaps you have been told at some time by your teacher or your parents not to *day dream* so much. What is the difference between "day dreaming" and the kind of dreaming Columbus and the Wright brothers did?

Columbus wanted to grow up so that he could follow his dream. What do you want to do when you grow up? What can you do now to help prepare yourself?

This poem has six stanzas. There are four lines in each stanza, and the last words in lines 1 and 2 and lines 3 and 4 rhyme. You may want to make a choral reading of the poem. High voices could read the first three stanzas. Deep voices could read the last three stanzas. Choose one pupil to be the young Columbus. Have him read the words in italics in the first three stanzas. Choose another pupil with a lower voice to be Columbus in the last three stanzas.

THE GREAT TREATY

Virginia Haviland

William Penn was a member of a wealthy English family. He gave up wealth and title to become a Quaker. In 1682 he and his group of colonists landed on the banks of the Delaware River to found the city of Philadelphia and the state of Pennsylvania.

The new colonists discovered that there was plenty to eat. The Indians were helpful. They often supplied the settlers with corn which they had raised, and sold them venison at a low price. In the rivers were fine large fish which made good eating. The men made themselves a great net in which to catch the fish. During the autumn, women and children gathered delicious wild fruits and nuts. All winter there were wild birds—partridges, turkeys, ducks, and geese. And, like the Indians, the colonists trapped otters, minks, muskrats, wolves, and foxes, so that they might send the furs to England to be sold.

"The Great Treaty" from *William Penn, Founder and Friend*, by Virginia Haviland. Copyright, © by Pierce and Smith. Used by permission of Abingdon Press, publishers.

The settlers were content with their new life. During the first winter they found much to be grateful for, even though they missed the friends and families left behind. They did not have to defend themselves against Indian raids as settlers had to do in some other colonies. They liked the climate better than the dampness of England. Penn later described a fall "like a mild English spring," followed by a "sharp, frosty winter" and a "sweet spring." Some colonists, to be sure, grumbled about the loss of conveniences. But with plenty of food and fuel they were comfortable enough. In Quaker meetings members told of their joy and peace in the new land. . . .

Penn did not lose any time in becoming acquainted with his Indian neighbors. Soon after he arrived, he went to visit them in their villages. Long before, he had written from England inviting them to attend an important council of Indians and white men. Now, personally, he asked them to come to the meeting in late November.

This great council of Indians and white men was to be held at Shackamaxon, an Indian village about a mile from Philadelphia, on the Schuylkill River. Shackamaxon meant "place of kings." Here the red men often had made treaties among themselves.

On the day set for the council, Penn and his party came up from Philadelphia on a barge. The governor's wide pennant fluttered on the masthead. Men pulled the barge up on the sandy beach and, led by Penn, walked to the council fire. Beneath a great old elm it blazed, in an open stretch of grass which reached to the surrounding forest. Near it waited representatives of three Indian nations—the Delaware, the Iroquois, and the Shawnee.

The Indians' skins were dyed in gorgeous colors. Bright feathers adorned their heads. In front sat the great and

good leader, Taminend, sachem of the Delawares. He was surrounded by old chiefs and councilors. Behind them were the younger braves and the women. Circle after circle of Indians widened outward, stretching back as far as the forest. Around the edge were aged women and children, looking with wonder at the pale visitors. No one carried a sword or bow, for no warlike weapons were allowed at the council fire.

William Penn led into the circle his councilors, his secretary, Markham, his surveyor-general, Holme, and a few of the earliest Dutch and Swedish settlers. They were dressed in their finest clothes. Their coats reached to their knees and were decorated with buttons and ribbons; their trousers were slashed at the sides. Ruffles decorated necks and wrists. William Penn wore a sky-blue sash to mark himself as governor.

The white men placed upon the ground their presents for the Indians. Then William Penn advanced. Tall and handsome, he strode across the carpeting of fallen leaves to the council fire. A simple honesty shone through his dignity.

Taminend, also looking very distinguished, rose and put a wreath on his head. In this wreath a small horn was twisted, as a symbol of his rank and authority. He turned

245

the pipe of peace, called calumet, devoutly toward heaven and earth, then smoked it. Next the pipe was handed to Penn and to all the members of the council. Each took it with care and smoked for a short time. Since red was the color of war, white clay had been daubed over the large red-marble head of the pipe, and the blackwood stem had been decorated with a ribbon on which was a design of white corals and colored porcupine quills.

One of the Swedish colonists acted as interpreter. He announced: "Taminend will hear the words of Onas." This was the Iroquois' name for Penn, as Miquon was the Delawares'. Both names meant *quill* or *pen*.

Slowly William Penn rose and spoke. "The Great Spirit rules in the heavens and the earth," he said. "He knows the innermost thoughts of man. He knows that we have come here with a hearty desire to live with you in peace. We use no hostile weapons against our enemies—good faith and good will toward men are our defenses. We believe you will deal kindly and justly by us, as we will deal kindly and justly by you."

Then, from a roll of parchment, he read and explained the conditions of the treaty:

1. We will be brethren, my people and your people, as children of one father.

2. All the paths shall be open to the Christian and the Indian. The doors of the Christian shall be open to the Indian, and the wigwam of the Indian shall be open to the Christian.

3. The Christian shall believe no false stories; the Indian shall believe no false stories; they shall first come together as brethren and inquire of each other; when they hear such false stories they shall bury them in the bottomless pit.

4. The Christian hearing news that may hurt the Indian, or the Indian hearing news that may hurt the Christian, shall make it known from the one to the other, as speedily as possible, as true friends and brethren.

5. The Indian shall not harm the Christian, nor his friend; the Christian shall not harm the Indian, nor his friend, but they shall live together as brethren. As there are wicked people in all nations, if the Indian or the Christian shall harm the one or the other, complaint shall be made by the sufferer, that right may be done; and when right is done, the wrong shall be forgotten and buried in the bottomless pit.

6. The Indian shall help the Christian, and the Christian shall help the Indian, against all evil men who would molest them.

7. We will transmit this League between us to our children. It shall be made stronger and stronger, and be kept bright and clean without rust or spot, between our children and our children's children, while the creeks and rivers run, and while the sun, moon, and stars endure.

After the interpreter had translated this for the Indians, William Penn continued:

247

"We will not be to you as brothers. Brothers sometimes contend with brothers. We will not be to you as fathers with children. Fathers sometimes punish their children. Nor shall our friendships be as the chain that rust may weaken—but I will consider you as the same flesh and blood as the Christians and the same as if one man's body were to be divided into two parts. We will go along the broad pathway of good will to each other together."

The Indians listened in silence, as was their custom. Then they consulted together. Finally Taminend motioned one of his chiefs to answer. The chief rose, came toward William Penn, and saluted him in Taminend's name. He took Penn by the hand and in his Indian language promised kindness and good will. "It is Taminend's mind," he said, "that this pledge shall be accepted and kept by us forever, and that the Indians and Christians shall live together as long as the sun gives light to the heavens."

Then, to show they accepted the white man's promise, the chief handed to Penn a wampum belt. It was large and

neatly made of eighteen strings of shell beads woven together. In the center was a picture, made in dark violet beads, of two men clasping hands. They represented Penn and Taminend. The governor was shown wearing a hat, and Taminend as a thinner man with uncovered head.

Dancing and contests of running, jumping, and throwing completed this historic ceremony. Penn and his men joined in all of them and in the feast that followed.

When settlers in other American colonies heard of the treaty, some of them laughed at William Penn for bothering to make an agreement with Indians. They laughed at him, too, for asking the Indians' permission to live in their country, and for paying the red men for their land.

249

Later on men did not laugh, for this treaty of Shackamaxon was the only treaty between red men and white men that was never broken.

WHAT HAPPENED?

William Penn came to this country in 1682. How long was this after the Pilgrims came? The Indians helped the Pilgrims. They also helped Penn. What did they do to help the Penn colony?

Penn held a council with the Indians. It was a great success. Why do you think Penn was so successful in his council? There were seven conditions in the treaty that was signed. Can you tell four of them? How did Taminend show Penn that he accepted the terms of the treaty?

THINK IT OVER

The treaty between Penn and Taminend was never broken. Why do you think this treaty was never broken?

Personal liberty has always been very important in our country. Penn respected the rights of the Indians and did not try to take away their personal liberty. How does lack of respect for personal liberty cause trouble? What points in Penn's treaty could be used in a treaty today?

Some colonists laughed at Penn for bothering to make an agreement with the Indians. People laughed at the Wright brothers for their dreams. We all know that no one likes to be laughed at. Why, then, should we be careful about laughing at someone else?

The signing of the treaty would be a good scene to dramatize. How would you make this scene into a play? What would you show?

UNIT SIX

Faraway Times and Places

OPEN RANGE

Prairie goes to the mountain,
  Mountain goes to the sky.
The sky sweeps across to the distant hills
And here, in the middle,
  Am I.

Hills crowd down to the river,
  River runs by the tree.
Tree throws its shadow on sunburnt grass
And here, in the shadow,
  Is me.

Shadows creep up the mountain,
  Mountain goes black on the sky,
The sky bursts out with a million stars
And here, by the campfire,
  Am I.

Kathryn and Byron Jackson

"Open Range," reprinted by permission from *Cowboys and Indians* by Kathryn and Byron Jackson. © Copyright 1948 by Golden Press, Inc.

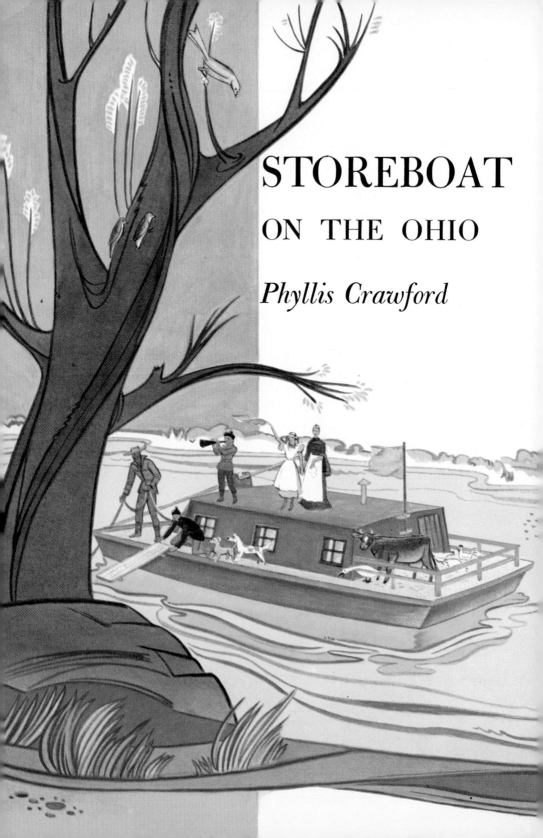

STOREBOAT
ON THE OHIO

Phyllis Crawford

The Doak family decided to run a storeboat on the Ohio River. Besides Mother and Father Doak, there were Susan, sixteen years old, Steve, thirteen, and ten-year-old David.

At last on Monday, the twenty-fourth of March, 1817, the storeboat was ready. As soon as Father brought the news, Mother put on her bonnet and cloak and they went to the schoolhouse to fetch Susan and the boys. . . .

Too excited to speak, the family tramped westward along the plank sidewalks. When they arrived at the banks of the muddy Monongahela, the storeboat lay before them, rocking gently with the current. She was a big broadhorn painted slate blue. The six small casement windows, three on each side, were trimmed with bright red. A red canoe rested on the deck against the rear wall of the cabin, beside the ladder. At the forward end of the boat was a fenced enclosure for the livestock.

Susan gasped. "Why, she's bigger than any boat on the river! She looks like Noah's ark." . . .

The boat smelled of new clean pine wood. Climbing down the hatchway, they found themselves in the store. It was a big room with windows on two sides, and shelves lining the walls from floor to ceiling. There were two long counters, one on each side of the room, and a stepladder for reaching the top shelves. . . .

"Storeboat on the Ohio" from *Hello the Boat* by Phyllis Crawford. Copyright, 1938, by Holt, Rinehart & Winston, Inc.

253

They peered into the little rooms and then walked into the big kitchen. An iron cooking stove was already set up in the center of the room with its pipe running up through the ceiling. There were two windows on opposite walls. In a corner facing the doorway, three steps led up to the little door which opened into the pen at the bows. Most of the wall space was taken up by cabinets and shelves. There was even a row of pothooks waiting for the cooking pots.

Mother looked about with a practiced eye. "I guess we'll be very comfortable here, George." . . .

At last the store was ready. The shelves were piled high to overflowing, the counters were scrubbed, and the floor was swept. The aroma of fresh clean fabrics, spices, and well-cured leather mingled with the resinous smell of the pine.

Father climbed the steep stairs to the roof and came back down, scanning the shelves as though he had never seen them before.

"It looks elegant," he said, rubbing his hands. "The first thing you see is the cloth, all the colors of the rainbow. Altogether it looks like a fine choice of wares." . . .

In each bedroom was a chest of drawers. Mother and Susan unpacked the clothes from the portmanteaus and one of the trunks and laid them away neatly in the drawers. Father stacked all the other trunks in one corner of his and Mother's room, where there was plenty of space.

"Now," said Mother, shutting the last drawer, "I guess that's all for today, except supper and the milking."

Father dusted off his hands. "No, there's one thing more. We haven't a flag."

He went into the store and snipped off a large square of yellow calico.

"There," he said, handing the calico to Susan. "You can

hem it to keep it from fraying, while Steve and I put up a flagstaff at the bows."

Susan turned the piece over in her hands. "But, Father," she said, "wouldn't a red flag look better? It would match the trimming on the windows, and the canoe."

"Red would look better," Father admitted. "But only grocery boats fly a red flag. Yellow means dry goods, and that's us."

By sundown everything on the storeboat was in order. Bessie had been milked, and the pailful of warm frothy milk had been poured into a shallow milkpan to let the cream rise. The chickens and the geese had hopped up on their low roosts and settled down for the night with contented murmurings and cluckings. . . .

By next morning they were awakened by the crowing of cocks up and down the river. Their own cock flapped his wings and tried to outcrow a rival on a nearby raft which housed a family of eight New Englanders, two tabby cats, a horse, three cows, five hogs, and a large number of chickens.

After a hurried breakfast, the Doaks flew to their chores. By the time the sun had begun to shine weakly through the haze of smoke over Pittsburgh, the dishes were washed, red Bessie was milked, and the featherbeds had been shaken out of the window. The bills of the fowls drummed on the deck as they pecked at their corn.

"All hands on deck!" Father cried. "Here we go. David, cast off the fasts. That's right. Now jump on board before she swings out from shore. Steve, take the right sweep, Susie, the left. I'll man the steering oar." . . .

The storeboat creaked and groaned her way into the channel of the Monongahela. Once in the current, she moved smoothly down the muddy river. . . .

255

Men looked up from their work along the banks and shouted. Small boys flourished their woolen caps. Housewives leaned over their back fences and waved their calico aprons. And the yellow flag at the bows fluttered in the morning breeze. . . .

Steven got the big red tin horn and blew until he was dizzy.

"That's to scare off the devil and secure good luck," Father explained. "We're on the Ohio River now."

After dinner the boys romped up and down the narrow deck with the dogs, while Susan washed the dishes. Just as she set the last iron pot on the stove to dry, she heard the blast of an unfamiliar horn and ran up to the roof to see what was happening.

A dark keelboat was skimming down the river with the brisk wind behind its square sail. The keelboatmen, in their gaudy red flannel shirts, blue jerkins, and coonskin caps, lounged on the deck, playing with a pack of battered cards. One man was steering.

They began to sing hoarsely:

> Hard upon the beach oar!
> She moves too slow!
> All the way to Shawneetown,
> Long time ago!

"Hello, alligator-horses!" David called out shrilly. "Half horse, half alligator!"

The boatmen roared with laughter. "That's our name," one of them bellowed.

"If you know anybody that wants a fight, we're spoiling for it. We're from Kentuck, and we're so tough that iron melts in our mouths."

"Keep to yourselves this time," Father shouted. "There's ladies aboard."

"That young one ain't no lady," another boatman bawled. "That's an angel!"

Susan blushed to the roots of her dark curls. Steve chuckled and gave her a dig in the ribs.

One of the boatmen leaped to his feet and pointed at Father.

"Suffering turnip seeds! If it ain't an optical pollution, that's George Doak without his red whiskers. The old goggled-eyed ring-tailed roarer!"

The rest of the crew cheered and waved their fur caps.

"Shut up, you son of a stuffed monkey," Father yelled good-naturedly.

The keelboat speedily left them behind, but the shouts continued until it sailed around a bend in the river.

"You know everybody on the river, don't you, Father?" said David admiringly.

"Hardly, Bub. But a flatboatman sometimes collides with the keelboatmen in the river towns."

"Did you ever fight with them?"

257

"Well, don't tell your mother, Bub, but there's times when a rough-and-tumble is the only path out of the wilderness."

"My peace-loving husband!" Mother's voice floated out through an open window.

Father grinned. "I don't fight when your mother's around. I've got religion now."

Steve hitched over to the center of the roof to rest his back against one of the rain barrels. "Did you ever wear the feather in your cap, Father?"

"What does that mean?" asked Susan.

Steve and David groaned.

"What on earth do girls talk about, anyway?" said Steve. "Why, when a boatman has licked his whole crew he can wear a red feather in his cap."

"Oh," said Susan. "Did any of those keelboatmen wear a feather?"

"No," said Steve promptly.

"Did you ever wear the feather, Father?" she asked.

"Feather-father, feather-father," David chanted. "That's very funny. Feather-father."

"Did you, Father?"

Father smiled reminiscently. "Once, on my second trip down the river. I had a gang of cutthroats for a crew, headed by a bandy-legged bully. He claimed I had promised them a whole gallon of rum a day throughout the trip. So I had to lick the lot of them."

David's mouth dropped open. "I wish I'd been there. I would have helped you."

"You were a baby in arms then, Bub."

"Well, anyway, I would now. Father, do you reckon you could buy me a coonskin cap like the ones the alligator-horses wear?"

"I'll see," Father promised.

"I wouldn't mind having one, too," said Steve. "These woolen caps look silly on the river."

Father took one hand off the steering oar to rub his eyes.

"I'm getting groggy from watching the river too long. Will you take the oar a while, Red? And, Davie, you sit down at the bows and watch for snags. I'm going to take a nap."

"I think I'll go below and look over the account books," Susan said, "unless the boys need me."

"All right, come along."

Father paused halfway down the hatch. "Look out for Dead Man's Riffle somewhere along this winding stretch. You'll see the island, and you'll recognize the riffle by the churning of the waters. We shouldn't have any trouble in high water, but you'd better call me."

"All right, Father." Steve's eyes shone. "This is fun."

David walked forward and sat down beside the short flagstaff, swinging his feet over the edge of the roof. Bessie clumped across her pen and licked his shoes with her rough tongue. One of the geese spread her white wings and hissed. Now and then the yellow flag brushed against his tousled sandy hair.

"Steve, what would you do if a steamboat came round the bend?"

"I reckon I'd holler for Father. They stir up the water something terrible."

259

Steve planted his feet wide apart and gave the steering oar a slight twist to see how it felt. The boat creaked and started to swing. He hastily righted the oar and she straightened again.

"What happened?" David asked.

"I was just trying her out."

"You'd better not. Something might happen and Father would be mad."

"I can handle her, no matter what happens. The current carries her along."

"Steve, where do you suppose the *Oliver Evans* is now?"

"You mean the *Constitution*. She'd be halfway from Louisville to New Orleans by now. But I wouldn't be surprised to see her grounded somewhere. Her keel's too deep."

The storeboat rounded another turn.

David sat up straight. "Isn't—isn't that an island ahead? The water looks rough."

"I guess that's old Dead Man's Island, all right. Watch me take her down the riffle all by myself."

"Steve! You'd better not. I'm going to call Father."

"Baby! Watch me and you'll find out how to handle a boat."

David flung a look at Steve's freckled face, braced himself on the edge of the roof, and watched the island approaching.

Steve gritted his teeth and steered for the channel which led past the island. When the storeboat reached the riffle she seemed to leap forward. He turned pale and took a firmer grip on the steering oar. He glued his eyes to the waters ahead, looking for the smooth streak that indicated the channel. The oar turned itself in his hands as he let the boat follow the twisting path.

David clung to the flagstaff and began to whimper.

Bessie gave a disturbed moo and rolled her soft red-brown eyes. Down below, the dogs whined and crockery rattled on the shelves. The little kitchen door opened against Bessie's flank, and Mother looked up at David.

"What's the matter? Why—" She gasped and steadied herself against the door-frame. Then she lowered her voice. "Be quiet, Davie boy. Don't upset Steve now. He may make out, the little blockhead. Why didn't you call your father?"

At last the island was behind them. As suddenly as the current had laid hold of the boat, it released her to float quietly once more.

Mother blew a sigh of relief, and went back into the kitchen. David let go of the flagstaff and sat up.

Steve relaxed his hold on the oar, and found that his

hands were numb and his shoulders ached. His knees began to tremble. Then he noticed Susan's bright brown eyes watching him from the hatchway.

"Here, take the oar," he said desperately.

She ran up the ladder and took his place. "I would have waked Father if you'd had any trouble," she said quietly.

He grinned weakly and sat down on the roof. "I thought I'd be so smart. I wonder what Father will say."

Suddenly David shrieked. "Look out! There's a mark on the water ahead. Maybe it's a rock."

Steve jumped up and took the steering oar out of Susan's hands. "It couldn't be a rock. The water's too high. Oh!"

Something raked the bottom of the boat along her entire length. The stern rose a little, and the rain barrels slid toward the bows. Down below there was a clatter of falling pots and pans. The animals set up a commotion—barking, mooing, cackling, honking. Then the boat settled back and remained there.

Father came running up the ladder, rubbing his eyes. "What's all this?"

Steve was still clinging to the handle of the oar. "I guess we're grounded, Father," he said in a small voice.

Father looked around and blinked. "Why, we've passed the riffle! How—why, you flea-bitten little idiot! Do you mean to tell me you brought her down the riffle?"

"Yes, sir, I guess so."

Father took out his faded blue bandanna and mopped his forehead.

"We ought to get down on our knees and thank God," he said. "If the wind had shifted against you, or if you'd been a little stronger on the oar, you couldn't have done it."

"I guess I deserve a licking, sir."

"I want you to look back there at the riffle," said Father.

"Do you see those dark spots under the water? Rocks. Last summer I saw a storeboat grounded near the left bank. They had to carry everything in the boat to shore, and it took them two days to mend the keel. Now do you see why I asked you to call me?"

"Yes, sir. I guess I just wanted to show you I could handle a boat. But I reckon we're stuck on a rock now."

"There's no rock here," said Father.

"Whatever it is," said Susan earnestly, "it's all my fault."

"I saw something," David put in excitedly, "and I hollered."

"Dave and Susan ain't to blame," said Steve. "I had the oar at the time."

"I didn't give it back to him soon enough, Father," Susan insisted. "That's why it's my fault."

Mother spoke up from the hatchway. "Why not finish the argument afterward? I need help down here. Brownie and Patch are doing the best they can, lapping up the broken eggs, but they refuse to use the mop."

"We'll be with you in a minute, Miss Biddy," said Father. "Now let's find out what's wrong before we spring a leak. Stand to your oar, Stevie. Don't let the current swing her about. Susan, jump down there in the pen and help out with the gouger. Dave, you and I will take the canoe and paddle around till we find out what's holding us."

When they had paddled halfway down the length of the boat, Father pointed.

"There it is."

"What is it?" Mother called from the window.

"A sawyer—a tree brought down by high water, with its roots caught in the bed of the river. The trunk rises and falls with the current, so sometimes you're on it before you can see it."

"I didn't see anything but a mark on the water," David said.

"Don't worry about it, Bub. Sometimes you can't even see that much."

"What do we have to do, Father?" Steve asked. "Dive down and saw off the tree?"

Father peered down through the water. "It looks like a lucky chance for us. The top of the tree is pointing downstream. I reckon we could heave off if we could touch bottom with the sweeps."

He paddled back to the stern, and he and David hoisted the canoe to its usual place on the deck.

Father plunged one of the sweeps into the water and groped for the bottom. Finally he located an embedded rock, and leaned his entire weight against the sweep. The boat scraped, swung in an arc, and floated free.

"Straighten her!" Father yelled. "That's right."

"Hurray! Hurray!"

"I'll take the steering oar now," said Father. "Steve, you look green about the gills. You'd better go below and help your mother pick up the pieces. We've had two narrow escapes."

"I'll never do a thing like that again," said Steve, as he stumbled down the hatchway.

"I'm willing to lay a bet on it," said Father. "But at times I wish we had another boatman aboard."

WHAT HAPPENED?

The Doaks were going to run a storeboat. Name some of the things their boat carried. Susan wanted a red flag for the storeboat. Why couldn't the Doaks fly a red flag?

Mr. Doak had once worn a red feather in his cap. What did this mean on the river?

What words would describe the keelboatmen?

Father was concerned about Dead Man's Riffle. What is a riffle? Why did Steve decide to run the riffle by himself?

THINK IT OVER

Steve did not obey his father and call him before they reached the riffle. What might have happened to the boat? They finally were grounded on a log. From their conversation during this incident what do you learn about Father, Susan, Steve, and David?

Steve was able to meet the emergency that arose. Tell about an emergency you have faced and what you did.

The author of this story gives many details so that we can see the boat and know what life on the Ohio River was like.

Tell about those details which made the story seem real.
Many families today live in trailers. How are the storeboat
and the present-day trailer alike? How are they different?

THE BOATMAN DANCE

With a snappy swing   FOLK SONG

The boat - men dance,   The boat - men sing, The
And when the   boat - men   come   on   shore They

boat - men up   to   ev - ery thing.   Then dance the
spend their money and work for more

boat - man dance, O, dance   the boat - man dance,   We

dance all night   'til broad day - light, Go home with the

girls   in the morn - in'. O,   high row,   the boat - men row,

Float - in' down the   riv - er,   the   O - hi - o.

266

THE OLD COACH ROAD

Rachel Field

There's hardly a wheel rut left to show
The way the coach road used to go.
Trees straddle it and berries grow
Where coaches rumbled long ago,
And horses' hoofs struck sparks of light,
Many a frosty winter night.
Here gypsy faces, lean and tan,
Peered from some lumbering caravan,
Or peddlers passed with bulging packs
And sheep with sun aslant their backs.
Now, only berry pickers push
Their way through thorn and elder bush—
But sometimes of a night, they say,
Wheels have been heard to pass that way.

"The Old Coach Road" from *Taxis and Toadstools* by Rachel Field. Copyright, 1926, by Doubleday & Company, Inc.

PEDRO OF MEXICO

Marjorie Flack and Karl Larsson

Pedro was a Mexican boy. While his parents sold their pottery at the market, Pedro made friends with Bill Randolph. Bill, a boy from the United States, could not speak Spanish and Pedro could not speak English. Bill was to start school in Mexico and Pedro, who had never been to school in all his ten years, was to accompany Bill for a few days.

―――――――――――

A man came up and spoke in Spanish to Pedro and Bill. "Buenos dias. You are new boys, are you not?"

Bill could not understand him, but Pedro said, "This is Bill Randolph and I am Pedro; Bill's mother said we should ask for Don Miguel."

The señor called one of the boys from the line. "Lico," he said, "take these new boys to Don Miguel."

Pedro and Bill followed the boy named Lico into the building. He led them to a kind gentleman who sat behind a table. Don Miguel smiled as he saw them and spoke to Bill in English.

"Are you William Randolph?" he asked, and Bill smiled and said, "Yes, sir."

"Your mother spoke to me about you and said you would come this morning. Is this your friend Pedro who will visit with us for a few days?" asked Don Miguel.

"Yes, sir," said Bill.

"Pedro of Mexico" from *Pedro* by Marjorie Flack. Copyright, 1940, by Marjorie Flack and Karl Larsson and reprinted by permission of Harold Ober Associates.

Pedro stood still while they talked; his heart sank because he could not understand them.

Then Don Miguel turned to him and asked in Spanish, "Have you ever been to school before, Pedro?"

"No, señor," said Pedro.

"I am sorry we will not have you with us for more than a few days," said Don Miguel; "but if you listen carefully you may learn a great deal."

"Okay, señor," said Pedro, because he was proud to show off his English.

Don Miguel looked surprised. But when he saw that Pedro was trying to please, he said to him gently in Spanish, "It is better to use our Spanish words when you are not sure of English ones. After this say, 'Si, señor,' to me or, if you wish to use English, say, 'Yes, sir.'"

"Si, señor," said Pedro, not understanding why.

"Now I will take you to your teacher, Señorita Carranza," said Don Miguel in English to Bill. "You will have to be with the beginners at first. As soon as you can read and write and speak in Spanish, I will put you with boys your own age.

"Until then you do not have to come to school in the afternoon," he told Pedro in Spanish.

Don Miguel then took Pedro and Bill to a room filled with boys and girls. . . . Don Miguel said a few words to Señorita Carranza, and she smiled at them and spoke to Pedro.

"It is good, Pedro, that you can come with your friend William to help him understand, for I myself can speak no English. Now please take the two seats near the window, and both of you watch the class very carefully. Maybe by tomorrow you will be able to join in."

Pedro and Bill felt very much ashamed to be put with such little children. They felt tall and big beside them. But as they watched the children, they wondered how they could be so bright—Bill because they seemed to talk so fast and he could not understand them, and Pedro because he wondered how they could remember what letters and numbers meant. He knew that he had only four days to come to school, and he wondered how in those four days he could learn the ways of a scholar as his father said.

The morning went very quickly. . . .

Pedro and Bill ate their lunch in the courtyard. Pedro was surprised to see the American things which Bill called "sandwiches," and then he wondered how the lemonade kept cold in the bottle. He liked the little cakes with icing on them.

When they had finished their lunch, Pedro tried to tell Bill they did not have to go back to school. He was surprised how quickly Bill understood and picked up the lunch basket and said, "Okay!" Pedro grinned at this and said to Bill, "Yes, sir!" and Bill laughed. As they walked slowly along, Pedro wished they did not have to go right back to work at Señorita Adams' house. Perhaps she would not expect them back so early; but then he remembered she had said they must come directly home, so he hurried a little faster.

But Bill did not hurry, and suddenly he stopped and pointed to a crowd of people who were going toward the Church of Chavarietta. They were not going into the church; they were all going to a place back of it. From this direction the sounds of a band tuning up echoed in the still air.

"Come, let's see what is happening!" cried Bill, running toward the crowd and leaving Pedro to follow.

Pedro knew he must not lose Bill in the crowd. He called to him—"Bill, Bill, Bill!"—and ran after him.

Pedro caught up with Bill as he came to a little piece of flat ground back of the church. Around this flat place ran a high stone fence, making it a small arena. On all sides of the arena rose the ever-present mountains, brown and bare nearby but blue and purple as they rose in the distance.

Men and women and children were sitting on the dry hot ground of the hillside overlooking the arena. Outside the walls stood a small clump of trees, and tied to these were a dozen restless bulls. Everywhere men on horseback stirred up a great cloud of dust as they galloped aimlessly around the stone wall and now and then suddenly raced one another up the steep hillside. An Indian brass band was tuning up.

"It's the Charro meeting!" shouted Pedro.

Although Bill could not understand him, he could see what was to take place. "It's a rodeo!" he cried. "Three cheers. We can see a rodeo!"

They climbed up on top of the stone wall, where they had a fine view of the arena. Inside they could see men on horseback. They were riding around and waving lassos, and showing off their horsemanship. The Master of Ceremonies, dressed in a gorgeous gold-braided costume, rode in and out of the arena shouting instructions. All the while great clouds of dust rose lazily up the mountainside. Men, horses, and bulls were restlessly waiting for the show to start.

At last a great shout went up. "El toro, el toro, el toro!"

271

—"The bull, the bull, the bull!"—shrieked a thousand voices, for one of the bulls was now being driven along the outside of the stone wall. It entered the arena through a small opening, which was quickly closed with logs across it. The bull stood bewildered for a moment, then he started to paw the ground with his powerful hoofs. Around him rode the men on horseback, shouting and swinging their lassos over their heads.

Pedro held his breath as the bull suddenly lowered his head and dashed toward one of the riders. His great horns were coming closer and closer to the side of the horse. Now he was almost upon him! But the rider jerked his reins and touched his spurs to the horse, and the horse jumped aside just in time. Surprised, the bull went rushing on and, before he could stop, nearly crashed into the stone wall. Then he turned and faced the riders, pawing the ground, and again he attacked a rider only to have him escape.

Over and over, the maddened bull attacked always to miss, until the Master of Ceremonies gave a signal and one of the men threw his lasso around the bull's horns. Another lassoed the bull's hind leg, and then they pulled in opposite directions until the bull fell to the ground. There he lay panting and unable to kick or rise. A man fastened a strong rope around the bull's middle and tied it with a loop at the top of his back. The loop was just big enough for a man to slip his hand in.

Now the band stopped playing, and all was still in the arena. Pedro and Bill saw the Master of Ceremonies standing in the center of the ring, and in his raised right hand he held a pair of silver spurs. "Brave gentlemen!" he called. "Who is brave enough to ride this bull? On whose boots may I strap these silver spurs to mark him a brave and courageous man?"

272

On all sides of the arena Pedro and Bill saw young men and boys teasing and urging one another to try. Words grew hot and loud, but no one seemed eager to try.

Again the Master of Ceremonies called out, "What, are all of you cowards and old women?" he asked. "Is there not one brave man among you who will ride this bull?"

At last a young man stepped into the arena and said, "I will ride the bull!"

A great shout went up from the people. "Bravo! Bravo! Bravo!"

The band struck up a march as the spurs were fastened to the young man's boots, and now a group of boys carrying red rags came running into the arena. All this time the bull had been held on the ground by the lassos. Now the young man slipped his hand into the loop of rope on the bull's back and threw one leg over him. At that instant the two riders stopped pulling on the lassos and the bull jumped up, threw off the lassos in one leap, and tried to throw the rider off his back. Around and around he spun, kicking and leaping

273

into the air. The boys waved their red rags, coming closer and closer to the bull's horns as they grew braver. The dust became so thick that Pedro and Bill could see only a whirling mass of boys and red flags and rider and bull. The crowds were shouting so loudly they could hardly hear the march the band was playing. The bull was getting tired and out of breath and no longer charged at every red rag, but the young man still hung on. Now he was watching his chance to dismount. As the bull got close to the entrance, the young man swung himself gracefully from the bull's back and slipped out of the arena.

A tremendous cheer went up for the brave young man, and the tired bull was led away.

Pedro and Bill cheered until they were hoarse. Then Bill said, "Gee, I think I could do that. It looks easy. I rode a bronco on a ranch once." Bill in his excitement forgot Pedro could not understand and went on talking. "I think I will try the next one," he said. "You just watch me; I'll show them how cowboys do it!"

Pedro had no idea what Bill had said, but he smiled and replied, "Okay!"

"El toro, el toro, el toro!" shouted the crowd again, and now another bull was driven into the arena. This bull was little and black and moved in a quick, nervous way. This time the riders did not allow him to come as close to the horses as the first bull, because this one, although he was small, was more dangerous. At last he was lassoed and lay stretched on the ground. Again the band stopped playing and the Master of Ceremonies held the silver spurs aloft, calling, "Brave gentlemen, who is brave enough to ride this little black bull? On whose boots may I strap these silver spurs to mark him a brave and courageous man?"

Before Pedro knew what had happened, Bill had jumped

down from the stone wall and was running toward the
Master of Ceremonies in the center of the arena. A
tremendous roar rolled out from the watching crowds.
"Vive el Americano! Bravo hombre!" they shouted over
and over again.

Pedro jumped down from the stone wall and ran after
Bill, who was now having the silver spurs fastened to his
shoes. Nearby, the panting bull lay straining to free himself.

"Bill, Bill!" shouted Pedro. "Don't, don't!" he cried,
desperately trying to make Bill understand. But Bill paid
no attention to him.

"Go back, little boy. Get out of the arena," shouted the
Master of Ceremonies at Pedro. "You have no red rag."

With trembling fingers Pedro took his peso out of the
little purse he always carried with him and turned to a boy
nearby. "Here, I will give you my peso if you will let me
have your red rag and take your place!"

The boy, without a word, grabbed the peso in amazement,
handed Pedro his rag, and ran quickly out of the arena.

Now Bill's hand was in the loop of rope on the bull's
back. The band was playing a loud march.

"Vive el Americano!" shouted the crowd.

Then the bull sprang up, with Bill on top of him. With all four feet off the ground the bull shot up into the air. Then down he came, and now he was spinning like a top. Pedro could see Bill still hanging on. Now the bull bucked and twisted and kicked. Bill bounced like a rubber ball, but he kept his grip. Pedro soon learned how to wave his rag like the other boys. He was quick on his feet and soon he was as brave as any of them.

"Oh, Holy Sebastián," Pedro prayed, "keep Bill from falling; don't let him fall!"

The bull came to a dead stop.

"Jump, jump!" shouted Pedro to Bill.

Bill did not take the chance and suddenly, like a bullet shot from a gun, the bull charged forward, his feet beating the ground. Then again he stopped. Down went his head, and over it flew Bill. Then Bill was on the ground. He did not move. Not far away stood the bull, his head lowered, his hoofs pawing the ground. He was getting ready to charge!

Pedro was close to where Bill lay. He could see the riders coming to help, but the bull charged! Pedro sprang forward, holding out his red rag. On the bull came, thundering over the ground, headed for the red cloth. Now Pedro could feel the bull's hot breath. Quick as lightning, Pedro threw the cloth over the bull's eyes and sprang aside. Blinded, the bull thundered on, but Pedro had changed his course, and Bill was safe!

"Bravo, bravo, bravo!" shouted the crowd. Twenty lassos now caught the bull and he was thrown to the ground.

Pedro ran to Bill, who was stirring now. "Bill, Bill, Bill!" he cried, bending over him.

Bill tried to get up, but something was the matter with one leg. The Master of Ceremonies had come to speak to them.

"All right?" he asked Bill in English.

"Okay," said Bill, trying to be brave.

"You are a brave and courageous boy!" he said to Pedro. "What is your name?"

"Pedro," he answered. "I am afraid my friend has hurt his leg."

The Master of Ceremonies said, "He is fortunate to be

277

alive. I will put him on my horse. We must find a doctor."

Bill was very brave when they lifted him up on the horse. He tried to grin and said, "I'm okay!"

The Master of Ceremonies put his hand on Pedro's shoulder, faced the crowds, and called, "Bravo, Pedro! Bravo, bravo!" And the crowd answered back, shouting, "Bravo, Pedro, bravo! Vive el Americano!" Then the Master of Ceremonies led the horse out of the arena, with the band playing and the crowd cheering. "Vive el Americano! Bravo, Pedro!"

When they reached the entrance, an American man came running up to them, saying in Spanish, "I am a doctor!" Then he spoke to Bill in English, saying, "I think I'd better look at that leg of yours, and I will take you home in my car." He carefully lifted Bill into a beautiful American car and, after examining his leg, said, "Well, it is broken. I must put a splint on it. Grit your teeth; it will be over soon."

Bill reached out his hand for Pedro's hand, held it tightly, and said, "Okay!"

After setting Bill's leg, the doctor drove them through the streets. Crowds of people followed them, shouting, "Bravo, Pedro!" Pedro could hardly believe that he was really riding in an American car. It all seemed like a dream. . . .

It did not take the car long to reach Bill's home. There was his mother standing at the door, looking very pale.

"What has happened? What has happened?" she kept saying as the doctor lifted Bill out of the car.

"It's just a broken leg. Don't worry," he called to her.

Pedro followed them into the house.

When Bill was comfortable on a sofa, the doctor put his hand on Pedro's shoulder and, turning to Bill's mother, said, "This lad has just saved your son's life!"

WHAT HAPPENED?

Pedro and Bill had to stay with the small children at school. Why was this so? Was the reason the same for Bill and for Pedro?

Bill saw a rodeo. Pedro saw a charro meeting. But they were looking at the same thing. Bill thought he could ride one of the bulls. What happened?

Pedro bought a red rag so that he could help Bill. How did Pedro help?

THINK IT OVER

Quick thinking often saves us from trouble. Point out the ways in which Pedro showed quick thinking in the story.

Bill had to get used to a new way of life in Mexico. Tell some of the things that were different from his life in the United States. What could you do to make school life easier for someone who comes to your school from another state or from another country?

Don Miguel was surprised when Pedro said "Okay." Why did he suggest that "Yes, sir" would be a better thing to say?

You probably found a number of new words in this story. Some of them may be "desperately," "tremendous," and "ceremonies." Can you tell in your own words what each word means? Remember that the dictionary in the back of the book will tell you how to pronounce each new word and what the word means. Other words which may be new to you are "monastery," "tourist," and "interior."

Spanish words used in the story are *si, buenos dias, señor,* and *charro.* What do these words mean?

JOHN HENRY

John Henry was a real man who worked on the early railroads. So many stories and songs have grown up about his great strength that he has become an American folk hero.

This ballad tells of John Henry's contest with a machine. He wanted to prove that by using only a heavy hammer he could drill steel faster than the new steam drill. John Henry won, but the effort cost him his life.

Heavily

John Hen - ry was a steel driv - in' man, He died
John Hen - ry said to his cap - tain, "A —

with a ham - mer in his hand, Oh
man ain't noth - ing but a man. And be -

come a - long boys and line the track For
fore I'll let your steam drill beat me down

John Hen - ry ain't nev - er comin' back For
Die with the ham - mer in my hand.

John Hen - ry ain't nev - er comin' back.
Die with the ham - mer in my hand."

John Henry got a thirty pound hammer,
Beside the steam drill he did stand.
He beat that steam drill three inches down,
An' died with his hammer in his hand,
Died with his hammer in his hand.

They took John Henry to the graveyard
An' they buried him in the sand,
An' ev'ry locomotive come roarin' by
Says, "There lays a steel-drivin' man,
There lays a steel-drivin' man."

THE LITTLE TOY LAND
OF THE DUTCH

Author Unknown

Away, 'way off 'cross the seas and such
Lies the little flat land of the Dutch, Dutch, Dutch,

Where the green toy meadows stretch off to the sea,
With a little canal where a fence ought to be!

Where the windmill's arms go round, round, round,
And sing to the cows with a creaky sound.

Where storks live up in the chimney-top,
And wooden shoes pound, plop, plop, plop!

Where little toy houses stand in a row,
And dog carts clattering past them go!

Where milk-cans shine in the shiniest way,
And the housemaids scrub, scrub, scrub all day.

Where dikes keep out the raging sea,
And shut in the land as cozy as can be.

Oh, that little toy land, I like it much,
That prim little, trim little, land of the Dutch.

MONI, THE GOAT BOY

Johanna Spyri

Moni lived in Switzerland. Each day he took the goats of the village people into the mountains. Here he watched over them while they grazed on the mountain grass.

Early in the morning Moni came through the little Swiss village singing his song. The goats ran from their sheds to meet him as he waved his stick and called to them by name.

Rosy pink clouds were piled high in the blue sky. A cool morning breeze whispered about Moni's ears as he climbed upward. How pleasant everything was! Everything was just the way he liked to have it.

For almost two hours Moni and the goats climbed up and up. Finally they were high among the mountain peaks. The higher they climbed, the brighter everything looked. At last Moni reached a green mountain meadow. Here he often stayed for hours at a time while the goats grazed quietly on the grass about him. Sometimes Moni sat on a high rock from which he could see far down through the valley below.

Today Moni took his sack of bread and cheese and laid it in a small hollow in the ground. Then he lay down on the sweet-smelling grass.

Yellow rock roses and purple gentians peeped through

the green of the meadow. The sky was a deep blue. All around were high mountains. Their snow-covered peaks seemed to touch the very sky above. Moni lay still, whistling happily, and a soft mountain breeze cooled his warm face. The goat boy was happy.

Once in a while Meggie, the youngest goat, would come to rub her head on Moni's shoulder. Then she would give a loving bleat and cross over to rub his other shoulder. Sometimes other goats from the flock would come to see their goatherd. Each animal had his own way of showing love for Moni.

One goat named Brownie was Moni's own goat. When he came for his visit he walked around the boy slowly as if he were making sure that everything was all right.

Next came a young goat, gray in color, and close behind him a small white one named Swallow. She had been given this name because she was tiny and swift and seemed to dart past like a swallow flying by. Meggie's mother, a shiny black goat, moved more slowly. She stopped a few feet away from Moni, looked at him for only a second, and then went proudly away.

Great Sultan was the oldest and the largest of the herd. He always came bleating to Moni as if to say, "I am the leader of this flock, and I have come to talk things over with you." When Great Sultan came, the other goats moved away—all but Meggie, who crept under Moni's arm so that the big old goat could not reach her. Meggie knew that Moni was her friend.

The sunny morning passed. At last Moni sat up and leaned on the stick that he always carried to help him over

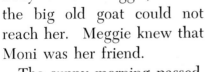

the rough climbs. "I wonder if we might try to climb a new side of the mountains this afternoon," Moni said to himself. "It would be fun to lead the goats up to the Three Dragon Stones. The grass is tender there."

Moni thought for a moment. The way was steep, to be sure, and there were dangerous places on the mountain climb. But he knew a good path, and the goats in his flock climbed carefully. So, after eating his lunch, Moni started up to the Three Dragon Stones with the goats climbing happily behind him.

Soon many of them had run ahead. Little Meggie, however, stayed with Moni.

For a while everything went well. Swallow led the way, jumping from rock to rock. Then, halfway up the steep climb, Swallow stopped suddenly. Facing her stood a wild chamois. Swallow was frightened, for she had never seen a chamois before. But Great Sultan came bounding up and pushed the chamois roughly to one side. Swallow kept on climbing, jumping swiftly from rock to rock.

Suddenly Moni called out in fright, "Swallow, what are you doing?" For the fast little goat had now climbed as high as the Dragon Stones and stood on the very edge of one of them.

Moni moved quickly. If Swallow took one step forward, she would fall many feet below. Hurriedly Moni climbed to draw her back to safety.

"Come with me, you silly," he scolded. Moni led Swallow down. Then he saw that Meggie had disappeared.

Suddenly he heard a faint bleat. It was Meggie's voice coming from below, a frightened cry for help. Moni lay down on the ground and leaned over the edge of the steep cliff. There, far below, he could see something moving. It was Meggie, hanging over the limb of a small tree that grew out from a crack in the cliff. Moni knew that Meggie could not stay on the branch very long, and if she fell she would be dashed to death on the rocks below.

Quietly Moni called to the little goat. "Hold on, Meggie. I will come to get you."

But the mountain wall was so steep that Moni could not climb down it. What *could* he do? Moni thought hard. Nearby was the Rain Cliff, an overhanging rock under which the goat boys sometimes gathered for shelter when a storm hit the mountains. The little goat, Moni thought, must be about on a level with the Rain Cliff. From there Moni thought he could climb upward to the tree where Meggie was hanging.

Quickly Moni whistled the flock together. Then he led them to a level place near the Rain Cliff and left them to graze while he went on by himself to the Cliff.

When Moni looked up, poor Meggie seemed very far above him. He knew it would be very hard to reach her, and still harder to climb back down with Meggie on his

285

back. But that was the only way to save the little goat.

The climb was slow and hard. But finally Moni reached the tree. Carefully he climbed out on the bough to which the frightened animal hung. Carefully he picked Meggie up in both hands and raised her to his shoulders. Then slowly he climbed back down.

When it was time to lead the flock home, Moni took Meggie in his arms. "You are still shaking, Meggie," he said to her softly. "You can't walk the long way home. I will carry you."

Moni carried Meggie all the way down. When the village people came to get their goats they were surprised at Moni's story. They had always thought that a goat boy did nothing all day but lie lazily in the cool mountain pasture.

WHAT HAPPENED?

Each goat had a different way of showing love for Moni. What was the name of the youngest goat and how did she show her affection for Moni?

Great Sultan helped Swallow. What did he do?

How did Moni save Swallow? How did he save Meggie?

The villagers were surprised when they heard what had happened on the mountain. Why were they so surprised?

THINK IT OVER

Why do you think the animals loved Moni so?

Children in our country have chores to do, but not many children work all day as Moni did. What kind of work do children do in the United States that is somewhat like Moni's work? What chores do you have to do?

Moni's country was very mountainous. What parts of our country look most like Switzerland?

UNIT SEVEN
Hero Tales

A SONG OF GREATNESS

When I hear the old men
Telling of heroes,
Telling of great deeds
Of ancient days,
When I hear that telling
Then I think within me
I too, am one of these.

When I hear the people
Praising great ones,
Then I know that I too
Shall be esteemed,
I too when my time comes
Shall do mightily.

Mary Austin

"A Song of Greatness" from *The
Children Sing in the Far West* by
Mary Austin, published by Houghton
Mifflin Company, and used with their
permission.

KING ALFRED
THE GREAT

English Legend

Long ago there lived in England a good and wise king, whose name was Alfred. Because of his goodness and wisdom, he has always been known as Alfred the Great.

Alfred was only twenty-two years old when he became king. Dark days were ahead of him. Fierce bands of sea robbers came across the North Sea from Denmark and made war upon the English. These Danes were strong and brave, and loved to sail over the seas in their long, black ships.

The English people feared them greatly, for they sailed up the rivers in England, waving their blood-red flag on which was the figure of a raven. They set fire to towns and villages, and sometimes even carried away children and made slaves of them.

The young King Alfred had to fight these invaders who were trying to conquer the whole English kingdom. For a number of years he kept them back and beat them in many a battle. But every year more black ships came, and things began to look darker for England.

One day after a fierce battle, the English soldiers were scattered and every man had to save himself the best way he could. King Alfred fled with one faithful servant who would not leave him. After crossing woods and swamps, they came at night to a woodcutter's cottage. They were tired and hungry, and the king begged the woodcutter's wife to give him something to eat and a place to sleep.

The good woman did not know the king. She thought he was somebody hiding from the Danes. She was sure he was

English because of his dress and his longbow. At first she was afraid, but when she saw how tired the two men were, she invited them into her hut.

She was cooking some cakes, and so she said to the king, "My poor ragged fellow, you shall have some supper if you watch these cakes. When they are done on one side, turn them, and see to it that they do not burn."

King Alfred sat down to watch them, and he turned them for a time, but his thoughts were on his people.

"How many little children are without homes tonight! How many of my bravest men are killed!" he said to himself.

He forgot all about the cakes. Finally the woman came in and saw that they were burned to a crisp.

"You lazy fellow!" she cried. "How dare you let the cakes burn! There is our supper all spoiled!"

The king did not say a word, for he knew he deserved the scolding. But just then the woman's husband, who had been one of Alfred's servants, came home.

"What is the matter, wife, and who is this?" he asked; for the room was dark, and he did not see the king's face.

"You may well ask. It is an idle fellow who does not know enough to keep the cakes from burning."

But the woodman fell on his knees before the stranger. "Hush, wife; it is our noble king."

The poor woman was frightened, for she knew she had treated her king badly. She threw herself at his feet and cried, "Forgive, forgive!"

"Peace, good woman," said the King. "You were kind to me and gave me shelter when I had nowhere to go. Tomorrow my servant and I will leave you to find a cottage for ourselves."

After a good night's rest, the king and his faithful servant set out into the forest. After many hours of weary tramping,

they came upon a poor little hut in the midst of tall pine trees. Here they made their home as best they could and lived on what little they could find to eat.

One day a loud knock was heard at the door.

The old servant did not dare to open the door, but called out, "Who is there?"

"One who is poor and very hungry. Will you help me?"

The servant went to the king and said, "My lord, there is a beggar at the door. What shall I do? Shall I send him away?"

King Alfred's heart was full of pity. "What food have we in the house?" he asked.

"Only a loaf of bread and a bottle of wine."

"Then give the poor man half."

The ragged beggar reached out his hand for the food, saying, "God will bless your master for his kindness."

The beggar's words came true. The fighting went on for several years, but finally peace came, and Alfred went about making his kingdom strong and happy. He built stone forts and castles to make his land safe. He made good and just laws, and built schools and hired learned men to

teach in them. He let no man be idle, and was never idle himself. Nor did the king forget the woodman and his wife. He gave them a beautiful farm with a home, barns, and many farm animals.

King Alfred died after a glorious and useful reign of nearly thirty years. It has been more than a thousand years since he died, yet the name of Alfred the Great is as dear to the hearts of Englishmen today as it was at the time he lived.

WHAT HAPPENED?

King Alfred was scolded by a woodcutter's wife. Why did she scold the king?

"God will bless your master," said the man who came to Alfred's hut in the forest. Why did the man say that?

THINK IT OVER

The words "God will bless your master" have been said in many different ways. For example, the Bible says, "Cast thy bread upon the waters: for thou shalt find it after many days." In other words, you are paid back for the good you do. What happenings, real or in stories, can you remember which show you how this idea works?

MY NATIVE LAND

Walter Scott

Breathes there the man with soul so dead,
Who never to himself hath said,
   "This is my own — my native land!"
Whose heart hath ne'er within him burned,
As home his footsteps he hath turned,
   From wandering on a foreign strand?

If such there be, go, mark him well!
For him no minstrel's raptures swell.
High though his titles, proud his name,
Boundless his wealth as wish can claim —
Despite those titles, power, and pelf,
The wretch, concentred all in self,
Living shall forfeit fair renown,
And, doubly dying, shall go down
To the vile dust from whence he sprung,
Unwept, unhonored, and unsung.

THE STORY OF
WILLIAM TELL

Katharine Scherman

William Tell was one of a band of Swiss patriots who
were trying to unite the states of Switzerland into a free
republic. Gessler was the Austrian governor of Switzerland,
whose cruel rule had made him a hated man. When
this story begins, William Tell and his son Walter are
in trouble. William has just failed to salute Gessler's
cap, which had been placed on a pike, as a symbol
of the Governor's authority.

"You have business in the new dungeon," said the second
guard, seizing Tell from behind. In a few seconds they
had bound his hands behind him and started to drag him
away. One of them grasped at young Walter, but he
slipped under the guard's arm and ran into the streets, calling for help. As if they had sprung out of the ground,
several hundred townspeople were suddenly in the square.
The guards found themselves hemmed in by a menacing
crowd.

Walter Furst pushed his way through the mob. "Be calm,
my friends," he said. "This can be handled peacefully."
He turned to the guards. "This man is my son-in-law, an
honest shepherd and hunter. He cannot have known of
the new rule, since his work keeps him always in the hills

"The Story of William Tell" from *William Tell* by Katharine Scherman. © Copyright
1960 by Katharine Scherman. Reprinted by permission of Random House, Inc.

and pasturelands. Here is money to set him free for an
unwitting offense."

"He has broken the law," said one guard stubbornly. The
crowd surged forward silently, the sun gleaming on hatchet
blades and knives. The guard turned pale. "All right. Let
him go free. But if the Governor had been here..."

"He comes!" cried the other guard. "Help! Mutiny,
murder, riot!" he yelled as a troop of horsemen galloped
into the square and stopped short before the solid mass of
townsmen. Behind them rode Gessler, his scarlet hunting
tunic edged with fur, his black boots shining.

"Drive the clowns apart," he ordered in a loud, harsh
voice. "Use your lances, and ride them down if you have to."

Their horses snorting and rearing, the soldiers pushed
through the crowd, laying about with their lances. The
people fell back, muttering angrily, and the guards drew up
their horses smartly in formation between William Tell and
the surly mob. The two guards of the cap, no longer frightened, told the Governor what had happened, and he turned
to the bound prisoner.

"At last we have caught the innocent mountain boy," he
said with a sneer. "The know-nothing hunter who hides
among the glaciers with the other mountain goats and smiles
even while he hatches secret plots against us. William Tell,

you have committed a sin against the divine Emperor, and you shall pay for it with your life."

Tell looked straight at the Governor and spoke with quiet politeness. "I have never knowingly committed a sin against the Emperor. If there was any crime today, it was the crime of ignorance. I ask your pardon."

"Well, I am a forgiving fellow. I will give you a chance to save your life. . . . Have I not heard that you are a master with the crossbow?"

Young Walter ran forward eagerly. "Oh, he is, sir! My father is the best archer in all Switzerland. He could shoot an apple off that tree, a hundred paces away."

Gessler smiled down at him. "You believe in the wonders your father can do, don't you, little one? You trust him?"

"I would trust him with my life," said the child.

"Then you shall!" The Governor turned to William Tell. "Prove your skill. Shoot an apple from the boy's head at one hundred paces. If you succeed, you will go free. If you miss, you will die."

The townspeople gasped in horror and the prisoner turned pale. "I would rather die now! Let your soldiers shoot me as I stand here."

Gessler laughed. "Listen to the brave and reckless hero! They say he takes a dozen chances every day in the mountains. Yet he turns coward over a single shot."

"I don't take chances with my son's life. I will not do it."

"Ah, but you must. For if you don't your son will be killed beside you."

"Am I then to be the murderer of my child?" He bowed his head.

Young Walter went to his father's side. "Don't be sad, Father. I am not afraid. I have seen you hit a bird on the wing. . . . Where am I to stand?"

"Tie the boy to that tree and bind his eyes," ordered Gessler.

"I will not be bound and have my eyes covered. I shall stand still as a rock and not draw a breath. I shall not even wink." Walter walked to the tree, picked an apple and laid it on his head. Then he turned and faced his father, and smiled. The prisoner's bound hands were freed and his crossbow handed to him. He tried to lift it, then turned to Gessler in agony.

"My fingers are trembling, and there is a mist before my eyes. Take my life now!" He knelt and bared his chest.

"I don't want your life," said Gessler scornfully. "I want the shot."

The townspeople cried, "Spare the boy!" and even Gessler's soldiers begged him to end the torment. They all crowded around the Governor, shouting and pleading.

Alone and unnoticed William Tell straightened suddenly and grasped his bow with a firm hand. Then one man turned and gasped, "He shoots!" The word ran through the square, and in a moment the crowd was still as if it had been turned to rock, all eyes fixed on the archer and the boy.

He did not hesitate. Deliberately he fitted an arrow to his bow, raised it to his shoulder, tautened the string and let fly. There was a small thud. Fearfully the crowd turned to Walter. Then a sigh like a small wind went over it. The boy still stood, and at his feet were two perfect halves of an apple.

Walter Furst ran forward and clasped his grandson in his arms. The people found their voices and raised them in a great glad cheer. Even Gessler was amazed. "Well done!" he cried, but William Tell did not move. Lonely and grim, he stared at the spot where his son had stood.

"You have won your life, proud archer," said the Governor. "You may walk home a free man, thanks to my generous forgiveness. But before you leave, one question. You took two arrows from your quiver. The second is still in your belt. What was it for?" Tell raised his eyes to the Governor but did not speak. "Come, tell me," the Governor repeated. "I have already given you back your life, and I promise that whatever you answer your life is still your own."

"Since I have your promise, I will tell you." Tell spoke sternly, looking the Governor straight in the eye. "If that arrow had struck my darling child, this second arrow was meant for you. It would not have missed."

Gessler turned red with anger. "I gave my word that you should keep your life. But I did not say where. Now that I know your murderous thoughts you shall be put where your arrow can never reach my heart." He ordered his guards to bind the prisoner with chains, hand and foot. "We shall cross the lake, you and I, to my castle on the other side. There I hold my court. And there I have a fine deep dungeon for you, where you can keep your life as long as you care to."

The ship was gaily painted, and the imperial flag flew proudly in the stiff breeze. But it was a small ship, hardly big enough for the Governor's courtiers and armed bodyguard. William Tell was chained to the mast, and his bow was put well out of reach, next to the steersman. The wind blew harder when the ship got out of the lee of the shore, and storm fog was creeping down the mountains.

299

To the left rose a line of jagged rocks where the waves flung themselves and exploded into towers of white spray. The fierce wind was driving the ship directly toward that terrible shoreline.

"Head her into the wind!" cried Gessler, terrified and angry. The oarsmen strained mightily, and the steersman tried to bring her around. But the little ship was like paper before the force of the tempest. The passengers crouched in the bottom, praying.

A soldier approached Gessler and spoke low: "We have one on board who can steer with miraculous skill. I myself saw him dare the storm in a tiny boat with an escaped murderer. Promise that prisoner at the mast his freedom, and he will bring us in through the rocks to a safe harbor."

"My promises mean nothing to him," answered Gessler. "Nor to me," he added with a wink. "But perhaps he will take one of my false coins in exchange for certain drowning."

William Tell was released. Without a glance at Gessler, he made his way through the moaning passengers to the tiller. Unhesitatingly he steered the ship straight toward land. The high black rocks loomed close. Spray dashed in his face, and the breaking waves roared. Skirting death, he searched the fog-shrouded shore. At last he found what he looked for — a solitary rock jutting into the lake, with a narrow ledge just at water level. He put out a foot and stealthily brought his crossbow within reach. Then he

headed the ship directly for the rock. Just before she hit he brought her stern around. Snatching his crossbow he swung himself onto the rock shelf, turned swiftly and thrust the ship away with his foot.

"You have met your masters, tyrant!" he shouted exultantly. "These waves will not obey your voice, and these rocks will not bow their heads before your cap."

Gessler's face, white and horror-struck, loomed up at the stern of the ship. "Save me!" he cried in a terrified scream. "My castles, my lands — all are yours if . . ." The ship was snatched away by a sudden shift of wind, and his voice was lost in the pounding of the surf.

William Tell crept up the steep, slippery rock, waves lashing at his back. He could not see the top, and did not know he had reached safety until his groping hands felt wet grass. With a sigh he knelt on the soft earth, touched the grass reverently, then lifted his arms to heaven. Something touched his back, and he turned to see a sheep nuzzling him. Other sheep stood near, gazing at him curiously. A figure came out of the mist, leather-clad and white-haired, carrying a tall shepherd's crook.

"Who are you, who have come up out of the lake? You can only be the ghost of one drowned, for no man could live on the rocks today."

"One could, Kuoni."

The shepherd came closer and exclaimed, "William Tell! We had already mourned you for lost. Indeed I saw the Governor's ship heading straight for the rocks. How did you escape?"

"I know the rocks. And if I missed the landing, it would be better to die there in the storm, fighting for my life, than to pass my days gazing at the blank walls of a dungeon. Never again to see the mountains or feel the wind — my soul would die before my body!"

WHAT HAPPENED?

The way you see this story in your imagination should be your very own. The pictures in your mind begin with the author's words. But you imagine much that the author does not say.

Remember how William Tell saved his own life and that of his son? How do you picture that moment? Describe what happened and how it happened. How did the people act? How did the town square look?

Think about William Tell's escape at sea. In your own words let others know just how you see the action, the people, and the setting.

THINK IT OVER

Now look back through the story and see what started your imagination moving. Choose five words which helped you most to see some action. Then pick five words which helped you to see the people. Finally, select five words which helped you to see some settings. Add a descriptive word of your own to each list.

THE ARCHER

Clinton Scollard

When May has come, and all around
The dandelions dot the ground,
Then out into the woods I go,
And take my arrows and my bow.

Of hickory my bow is made,
Deep in a darksome forest glade
Cut from a sapling slim and tall,
And feathered are my arrows all.

And sometimes I am Robin Hood,
That olden archer brave and good;
And sometimes I'm an Indian sly,
Who waits to shoot the passers-by.

So up and down the woods I roam
Till sunset bids me hurry home
Before the pathway through the glen
Is peopled by the shadow-men.

And when at night my bow unstrung,
Is close beside my quiver hung,
To bed I slip and slumber well,
And dream that I am William Tell.

"The Archer" from *A Boy's Book of Rhyme* by Clinton Scollard.

ULYSSES, A GREEK HERO

Clifton Fadiman

Long, long ago—perhaps three thousand years ago—a great war was fought between the Greeks and the Trojans. Many stories are told of that war and how at last it was won by the Greeks. Partly they won it because of the cunning and wisdom of one of the Greek heroes, the brave Ulysses.

After he and the Greek army conquered Troy, Ulysses ran into bad luck. It took him many years to return to his home on the rocky island of Ithaca, where he was king and where his wife Penelope and his son Telemachus had waited for many long years. During this time strange and wonderful adventures happened to him. The story of one of these adventures is what you are about to read.

After Ulysses had helped win the war between the Greeks and the Trojans, he and his followers boarded their ships, hoping to reach home quickly. But this was not to be.

For many days Ulysses and his small fleet were tossed about by roaring winds and violent waves. At last, tired and hungry, they approached an island, the land of the Cyclopes.

The Cyclopes were rude, savage giants, with no laws. They lived in stone caves in the mountaintops. They herded their flocks of sheep and goats, each alone, and rarely spoke

"Ulysses, a Greek Hero" from *The Voyages of Ulysses*, by Clifton Fadiman. © Copyright 1959 by Clifton Fadiman. Reprinted by permission of Random House, Inc.

one to the other. Each was many times the height of a normal man. Each had but one eye in the middle of his forehead.

If they hated the sight of one another, they hated strangers even more. But Ulysses did not know this.

He and his followers landed at night in a thick fog. They killed some of the Cyclopes' goats for food. After they had eaten, they rested the night through. In the morning King Ulysses gathered his men together.

"Friends," he said, "for the time being I want you to stay here. I will go with some of the men of my ship to find out what sort of persons these Cyclopes are, and whether they are friendly to strangers." He picked out the twelve best men in the company. He also took with him beautiful presents to give to the Cyclopes in return for their food and water.

When Ulysses and his men reached the stone cave of one of the Cyclopes, its owner was not at home. They entered

NAMES IN THE STORY

Cyclopes (sī klō′pēz), a race of lawless one-eyed giants.
Penelope (pə nel′ə pē), wife of Ulysses.
Polyphemus (pol i fē′məs), a chief of the Cyclopes.
Poseidon (pō sī′dən), god of the sea.
Telemachus (tə lem′ə kəs), son of Ulysses.
Zeus (zōōs), chief Greek god.
Ulysses (yōō lis′ēz), a Greek warrior.

the wide, dark mouth of the cave. Inside it was dim and vast. There were baskets of cheeses everywhere, made from goats' milk. There were goats, too, tethered together, filling the cave with their bleatings.

It had taken many hours to find the cave upon the mountaintop. Ulysses and his twelve men were hungry. They killed a fat goat, sacrificed to the gods (for in those days they believed in many gods, not one, as we do today), and roasted it. They ate some of the cheese also, but they took no more than what they could eat in just one meal.

Then the Cyclops appeared, huge and terrible. He entered the cave and picked up a stone slab so heavy a hundred ordinary men could not have lifted it. With this he shut the mouth of the cave with as much ease as you close the door to your room. He lit the fire and spied Ulysses and his men sitting there.

"Who are you?" he asked. He had a voice like the deep roar of the wind on a mountaintop.

But the crafty Ulysses did not tell him everything. He spoke of his many adventures and asked for help in the name of Zeus, king of gods. But the Cyclops laughed.

"I don't care one bit for Zeus," he said. "I am much stronger than he and all your other gods." Then he jumped up, seized a couple of Ulysses' brave companions, killed them and ate them. For he loved human flesh.

Then he went to sleep, his snores filling the cave like thunder. The wise Ulysses sat with his remaining men and tried to figure a way out of the dark cave. They could not move the huge boulder. What was he to do?

In the morning the Cyclops awoke. Again he seized two of Ulysses' companions, killed and ate them. Satisfied with his breakfast, he went out, closing the mouth of the cave with the huge rock as he went. All that day in the damp darkness Ulysses and his men sat and thought. But they could not think of a way to get out of their prison.

The wise Ulysses looked about him. Lying close by was a huge trunk of green olive wood which the Cyclops used sometimes as a staff. It was so thick and heavy that it took all of Ulysses' strength and the strength of his men to lift it. They sharpened the staff to a needle point and hardened it in a fire they built. Then they waited.

When the Cyclops returned at night from pasturing his goats, Ulysses offered him a drink of special wine, which he had brought with him as one of the presents for these people, had they turned out to be kind and gracious. The Cyclops drank all the wine. It made him sleepy, and he stretched out in his usual resting place beside the fire.

Just before he began to doze off, the wise and crafty Ulysses spoke to him.

"Cyclops," he said, "you wanted to know my name."

"Yes," the Cyclops mumbled, half awake. "Mine is Polyphemus. Tell me yours and I will give you a gift."

"Call me 'Nobody'," cunning Ulysses replied.

"Good," answered Polyphemus. "Here is your gift. Of all your company, I will eat 'Nobody' last."

With a cruel chuckle he fell asleep, snoring.

Then Ulysses and his men quietly lifted up the sharpened staff and with all their might drove it into the eye of the

307

Cyclops, blinding him. He awoke with a terrible scream of pain and rage.

His yells brought other Cyclopes to his door.

"What is the matter, Polyphemus?" they cried out.

"Nobody has blinded me," yelled the Cyclops. "Nobody will kill me."

His friends all laughed at this.

"That's all right," they said. "If *somebody* had done these things, we would lift up the rock and come into your cave to kill him. But since *nobody* has done this to you, we will leave you. Please don't disturb us again with your shouting."

In spite of the Cyclops' cries, off they went.

Now Polyphemus pushed open the rock that guarded the entrance of the cave and sat in the doorway, his arms spread out. He hoped to catch Ulysses and his men as they tried to slip by him. But the cunning Ulysses had thought up another scheme. He went to the biggest sheep he could find and curled himself up under its shaggy belly, holding onto the wool. He ordered his men to do the same with the other sheep.

As the sheep filed out of the cave, the Cyclops could not feel anything except the sheep's wool.

So Ulysses and his companions were able to slip by the blinded monster, into the open air and freedom.

Once aboard their ship Ulysses remembered the deaths of his companions, and he grew angry. From the bow of the ship he yelled out to the blinded Polyphemus:

"If anyone asks you how your eye was put out, tell him that Ulysses blinded you."

The monster lifted his blinded eye to heaven and prayed to Poseidon, god of the sea, to bring disaster to Ulysses and his men. From Olympus, the home of the gods, Poseidon heard him. He grew very angry, for Polyphemus, the Cyclops, was one of his sons. Poseidon swore that he would do his best to make Ulysses' voyage as dangerous as possible. And so it turned out.

"Head for the open sea!" shouted Ulysses. The men bent to their oars, the sails filled, and so they left the dreadful island of the Cyclopes.

WHAT HAPPENED?

Ulysses used three tricks to escape from Polyphemus. Tell about each trick.

THINK IT OVER

Ulysses was a great hero to the ancient Greeks. From the way Ulysses acted, you can tell what qualities the Greeks admired. What qualities did they admire?

BEOWULF WINS A BATTLE

Gladys Schmitt

A great giant, Grendel, was killing men in the kingdom of Hrothgar, king of the Danes. From the land of the Geats came Beowulf and fourteen soldiers to help.

The light wind drove them over the springtime water. The ship met no misfortune. She flew to Daneland like a bird. There on the coast of Hrothgar's kingdom, on the beach under the gray cliffs, they took their weapons out of the vessel and gave thanks to God who had brought them there so luckily and so soon.

But they had scarcely unloaded when King Hrothgar's coast warden rode down to them. He had seen their shields and mail coats gleaming from his post on the cliffs above them, and feared they were enemies. His lean face was grim between his brown beard and his bright helmet. "For a long time I have stood guard on these cliffs," he said, "and no band of armed men has dared to land as openly as you. It will be best for you to tell me quickly what your business is in the land of my king."

Then Beowulf spoke like a determined captain, young though he was. "We come as friends from the land of the Geats," he said. "I am Beowulf, and my father was the famed warrior Ecgtheow. He did high deeds before death called him out of our house. His name is known throughout the world. Our errand is a blameless one. We are here to

"Beowulf Wins a Battle" from *The Heroic Deeds of Beowulf*, by Gladys Schmitt. © Copyright 1962 by Gladys Schmitt. Reprinted by permission of Random House, Inc.

save King Hrothgar from shame, to cleanse his mead hall and ease his woes. Do not hold us here or turn back. We bring with us better days for the warrior-Danes."

Then the grim warden smiled, for the young warrior was frank and fine to look upon. Courteously he rode before the strangers to show them the way to Hrothgar's hall. When they caught sight of its gleaming roof from the cliffs, he told them to march on without him. He did not dare to leave his post. His eyes were keen for enemies. And they went, fifteen good Geatish warriors in marching order, their soles ringing on the stones of the path, their swords and shields gleaming, their mail coats jingling, until they came to the broad terrace around the splendid hall.

There they were questioned by Hrothgar's herald and told to wait. And Beowulf could scarcely bear the waiting — there was such a longing in him to see the King. Because a stranger had come to him from a far land, Hrothgar decided to meet him in a stately fashion in the great hall, even though it had long stood neglected and unused. The King sat now with a few of his faithful Danes around him. And, when he had taken his place on his high seat, the herald came out and invited the stranger to follow him in.

NAMES IN THE STORY

Beowulf (bā′ə woŏlf′), a great warrior and a prince of the Geats.
Breca (bre′kə), a former opponent of Beowulf.
Ecgtheow (ek′thā ō), father of Beowulf.
Geats (gēts), a Scandinavian nation in what is now Sweden.
Grendel (gren′dəl), a giant monster preying upon the Danes.
Heorot (hā′ō rot), the palace or hall of the Danish king.
Hrothgar (roth′gär), king of the Danes.
Siegmund (sēg′mund), an ancient hero of the Danes.
Unferth (un′farth), a Danish warrior who is jealous of Beowulf.
Wealhtheow (wā əl thā′ō), queen of the Danes, wife of Hrothgar.

Shadowy it was, and sorrowful, too, in that mead chamber. There was a smell of dampness there, and slants of sunshine showed the ruin — the cobwebs, the dusty benches, the wrenched locks and hinges, the great iron bands reddened here and there by rust. Alone on his high seat, with his warriors at his feet, sat the good King Hrothgar. His beard and hair were fine and silvery like the webs spun by spiders. His face was netted over with countless wrinkles. His eyes, blue and faded, looked at the lad who had come so far across the sea.

He asked in a gentle voice who Beowulf was. He said, after he was told, that he had known the lad's father and mother. "And what do you mean to do for me?" he asked. "Surely you are not so reckless that you and your little band will sleep under this accursed roof and meet the monster Grendel here by night?"

Then Beowulf told him that he meant to do exactly that. And the lad looked so strong and tall, and his voice sounded with so brave a note that the tired king began to take heart. "Heaven bless you for your courage and your kindness," he said, and embraced the stranger as though he were a son. "You see how it is with me. My warrior band is ruined by Grendel. He has carried off many to their deaths and has frozen the hearts of the rest with fear. We can do nothing against him. Only God can deliver us, and it may be that you are sent by God."

At this all the Danish warriors nodded — all except one. That one, whose face was dark and sour, frowned at the young man. He was Hrothgar's favorite, and his name was Unferth. He sat closest to the high seat with his head near the King's knee. Black jealousy rose in him when he saw another man ready to do what he would not do himself.

King Hrothgar said, "The brave guests are weary and hungry. Clear a bench and bring them mead and meat. Call in a minstrel to sing of old, brave deeds. Such songs will give them courage and faith in themselves."

So a bench was cleared and a minstrel was summoned, and the kind Queen Wealhtheow came from her bower to honor the feast. For the first time in many years, merry noises sounded in Heorot. The meat was tasty and crisp, and the mead was pure nectar poured from a great jeweled cup. And the sight of the old King's happiness was so dear to Beowulf that he felt no fear, felt only a strong need to make his host happier still.

Then the sour-faced Unferth raised his voice and called from his seat of honor to Beowulf. "Are you not that Beowulf who had a reckless swimming match with Breca?" he asked. "I have heard that you two risked your lives like fools in the winter waters. I have heard also that Breca beat you at it roundly. *He* reached the goal, but *you* came back to shore a sorry sight."

Beowulf's throat tightened at that taunt. He longed to hurl his beaker at Unferth. But he mastered himself and said with dignity, "It is true that we were reckless, but we were only young pages then. It is also true that he reached the goal and I did not, though no man in Geatland would mock me for that. They know the truth. Ask, and they will tell you I slew nine sea monsters under the icy water. Ask and they will tell you they are grateful to me, glad that these

beasts I killed will never creep onto the shore or fall upon their boats and drag the mariners down to be eaten under the sea. Also, let me tell you this: If *you* were a man of courage, your king would not have grown old with grieving. *You* would have killed Grendel and cleansed this hall."

Once he had said it, he feared he had displeased the good Hrothgar. But the King only smiled, and Unferth blushed and held his tongue.

Then the minstrel struck up another song, and the merry noises rose again — the sound of the harp, the talk, and the laughter. The kind Queen Wealhtheow, faded by trouble but still beautiful in her embroidered robes and golden diadem, came down from the high seat. It was her custom to offer the jeweled cup of mead first to the King and then to his guests. When she brought the cup to Beowulf, she spoke to him in a clear voice. "I thank God that what I have hoped for is about to come to pass. I believe that you, dear stranger, will deliver us from our woes," she said.

And before he took the cup from her, Beowulf answered her with these words: "Lady, before I stepped from the shore of Geatland I had promised myself that one of two things would become of me. Either I would slay the monster or meet my death at grips with him in your husband's hall."

Then the noise of the feast slowly lessened, though it was still loud enough to reach the ears of Grendel under the loathsome fen water. The Queen went away to her bower, and the King followed her, and all the Danish warriors bade the strangers good night and went to sleep in some safer place.

With the others gone, the band of Geatish warriors seemed small. The light of day was quenched, and the torches died out. Beowulf's companions slept on cushions. They set their helmets on the benches above them, but wore their coats of mail and kept their swords under their hands. Beowulf did otherwise. He gave his mail and helmet, his sword and spear to a companion. "I will not make a shameful thing of the high arts of battle by using them against such a foul creature," he said. "Grendel uses no weapons, and neither will I. I will overcome him as he will strive to overcome me, with nothing but the might of my body and the grip of my naked hands."

It was no easy thing to fall asleep in the echoing blackness. Not one of them hoped to see again his people at home, his castle where he had been brought up, or the dear coast of his native land.

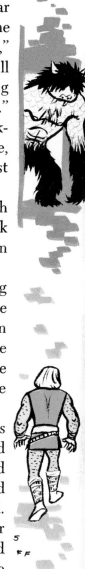

Then came Grendel in the dim night, splashing through the fen waters, tearing like a high wind through the black forests. He was headed for Heorot, and all there had fallen asleep — all but one!

Beowulf, wide-eyed on his pillow, heard the thudding feet, saw the big door fly open. The tremendous and horrible shape, the hairy creature, half man, half beast, showed in the doorway in the light of the misted moon. His eyes shone red, like murky fire. He laughed aloud to see such a fine feast, and the laugh was so dreadful that it froze even the hero's heart.

Before Beowulf could recover his courage, the monstrous paw of the man-beast snatched up the closest warrior, clawed him, tore him, flung him back onto the floor, his life's blood drained away. Then it reached again for the next of the good companions, but by this time Beowulf had himself in hand. He sprang up and gripped the devilish creature's paw. For the first time, Grendel felt terror. Never in his evil life had he felt such a grip. There was no courage in him when he was brought to the test. At once he tried to get away, but no matter how hard he shook and dragged he could not pull loose from the iron-strong hand.

315

Then the young hero did not fear the foul breath and the fiery eyes. He did not seek to keep himself from the hairy beast. He grappled with the creature brow to brow and knee to knee. And their grappling was so fierce that they turned over benches and cracked wall timbers and pillars.

By this time the others were awake. Armed, they came to their chieftain's help, laying about them in the blackness with swords. But swords could do nothing against the monster. Only the grip of Beowulf, still holding him fast, could bring him harm.

In that grip Grendel threw himself about so wildly that it was a wonder he did not bring Heorot down. Surely the hall would have been shattered if it had not been held by the iron bands. And just as Beowulf began to feel mortal weariness, just as the flesh began to split at his knuckles from the hardness of his grip, the monster uttered a blood-freezing yell. A crack had opened in Grendel's shoulder. The sinews there sprang wide. The covering of his bones spread apart. Shrieking, he pulled himself free and fled into the night. But he left something behind him. His hairy paw, his forearm, his upper arm as high as the shoulder remained at Heorot, held fast in Beowulf's gripping hand.

That gruesome trophy made Beowulf rejoice. With such a wound in his shoulder, it was plain that Grendel could not live to bring sorrow to the Danes. The young hero hung the arm of the monster beneath the antlers under the gable. Then he and his comrades lay down among the broken benches and shattered tables and slept.

That was a happy morning for the Danes. They rode out to follow the track of Grendel to the fens. They saw the lake blood-tinged again, but this time there was no weeping at the sight. Farmers and townsmen and warriors need no longer fear that their kinsmen's blood would stain the muddy waters. Women and children could stay out of doors in the evening and sleep fearlessly through the night.

The Danish warriors rode back to Heorot, praising Beowulf all the way. They said that he was like the greatest of their ancient heroes, the dragon-slaying Siegmund. In the pale light of the spring dawning, they spurred their horses for pure joy and raced each other on the new green turf. Truly, the stranger from afar had brought better days for the Danes!

WHAT HAPPENED?

When he met Beowulf, King Hrothgar was troubled and discouraged. Why was he so downhearted?

All the Danes in the great hall took courage from Beowulf, except Unferth. How did Beowulf silence Unferth?

That night saw Beowulf in a great struggle. Tell about that struggle and how it ended.

THINK IT OVER

This story was told long ago by some of the early peoples of England, the Anglo-Saxons. To add excitement to the tale, the Anglo-Saxons used many words with the same beginning sounds. So they might say: Grendel *f*led to the *f*ens.

The author of this telling of the story has kept true to the old Anglo-Saxon style. Find five pairs of words, each pair in different sentences, which repeat beginning sounds.

317

AMERICAN YARNS

Carl Sandburg

They have yarns
Of a skyscraper so tall they had to put hinges
On the two top stories to let the moon go by,
Of one corn crop in Missouri when the roots
Went so deep and drew off so much water
The Mississippi river bed that year was dry,
Of pancakes so thin they had only one side,
Of "a fog so thick we shingled the barn and six feet out
   on the fog,"
Of Pecos Pete straddling a cyclone in Texas and riding
   it to the west coast where "it rained out under him,"
Of the man who drove a swarm of bees across the Rocky
   Mountains and the desert and didn't lose a bee,"...
Of the sheep counter who was fast and accurate: "I
   just count their feet and divide by four,"
Of the man so tall he must climb a ladder to shave
   himself,
Of the runt so teeny-weeny it takes two men and a
   boy to see him, ...
Of John Henry's hammer and the curve of its swing
    and his singing of it as "a rainbow round my shoulder."
      "Do tell!"
      "I want to know!"

"American Yarns" from *The People, Yes* by Carl Sandburg, copyright, 1936, by Harcourt, Brace & World, Inc. and reprinted with their permission.

UNIT EIGHT
A Long Story

THE BRANCH

We stopped at the branch on the way to the hill.
We stopped at the water awhile and played.
We hid our things by the osage tree
And took off our shoes and stockings to wade.

There is sand at the bottom that bites at your feet,
And there is a rock where the waterfall goes.
You can poke your foot in the foamy part
And feel how the water runs over your toes.

The little black spiders that walk on the top
Of the water are hard and stiff and cool.
And I saw some wiggletails going around,
And some slippery minnows that live in the pool.

And where it is smooth there is moss on a stone,
And where it is shallow and almost dry,
The rocks are broken and hot in the sun,
And a rough little water goes hurrying by.

Elizabeth Madox Roberts

"The Branch" from *Under the Tree* by Elizabeth Madox
Roberts. Copyright 1922 by B. W. Heubsch, Inc., 1950 by Ivor
S. Roberts. Reprinted by permission of The Viking Press, Inc.

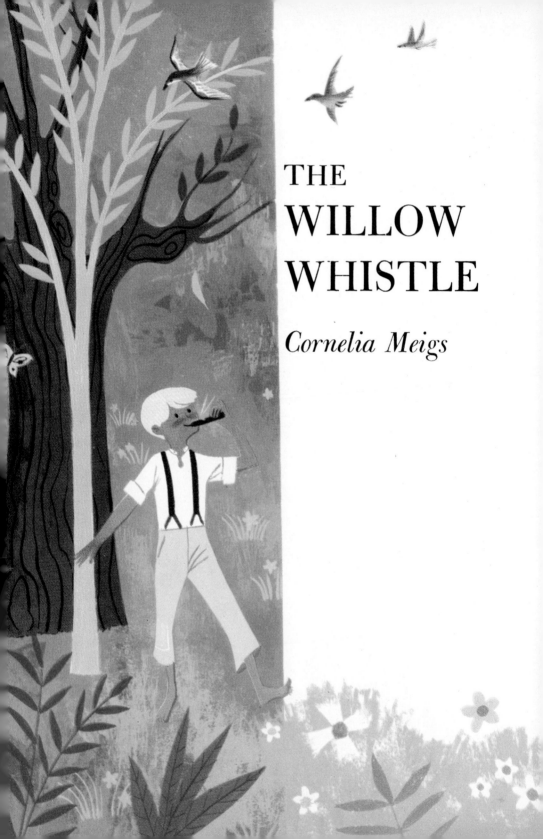

THE
WILLOW
WHISTLE

Cornelia Meigs

KIDNAPPED?

It was on the spring day that the willow trees were showing yellow beside the creek that Mary Anne first went out to play on the smooth meadow that sloped down to the stream. Through all the winter her mother had kept her most of the time within the house, the square log cabin at the edge of the prairie. Or she had allowed Mary Anne to play sometimes in the narrow door yard, fenced with brush and poplar posts to which the bark still clung. When the little girl begged to go beyond the gate and when even John Seabold, her father, added his urging to hers, Mary Anne's mother would only answer—

"I am afraid of the Indians."

"Indians are nothing to be afraid of," John Seabold would protest. "They are as peaceable as any neighbors we have." Often he would add, "And they are our most important neighbors, too. Until we show that we are friends with them and trust them, we will never prosper."

John Seabold had a long log building, half a mile away where the trail forked, which he kept as a store, and traded with the Indians of the Sioux tribe, exchanging cloth and beads, axes and guns, for furs, buffalo hides, and corn. He tried also to teach his brown neighbors better ways of living, how to take wiser care of sick children, or how to raise more grain and bigger squashes in the little fields that the women

The Willow Whistle by Cornelia Meigs. Copyright, 1931, by The Macmillan Company and reprinted by permission of The Macmillan Company.

hoed and tended. Sometimes he even tried to make them understand how much better off they would be if they could stop their endless quarrels with the other tribes who lived near them, particularly their great enemies, the Arickarees. But to that last advice they did not like to listen.

Mary Anne often sat in the corner of the store building and watched his customers go in and out, the shuffling squaws with great burdens on their backs, held by a deerskin strap across their foreheads, and the tall, light-stepping braves with feathers in their hair. Some of them came from scattered lodges nearby, some rode their ponies from a greater distance. They spoke very little, offering what they had to sell, pointing out what they wished to have in exchange. Mary Anne stared at their bright, black eyes and their unsmiling, red-brown faces and wondered what they were thinking.

"Do you believe they like us?" she would ask her father. John Seabold had always shown his red neighbors every sort of kindness and fair dealing. But to his little daughter's question he could only shake his head.

"They are not our enemies," he said, "but whether they are really our friends, we cannot know, except after a long time."

Mary Anne was not in the least afraid of them. At first all the dark faces looked to her just the same, but soon she

learned to know this one or that, and could also tell, from the feathers in the men's hair or the pattern of their beaded leggings and moccasins, whether they came from the nearer villages or from afar. John Seabold and his trading station were beginning to be known long distances away.

But Mary Anne's mother could not learn so quickly to put aside her dread of these wild creatures belonging to a new country. She had lived all her life in the safe, close-built streets of an eastern town, and she and Mary Anne had come only in the last autumn to live in the cabin that John Seabold had built for them in the newly settled prairie country. As the months passed, however, she began at last to be more used to all the strange things about them. Therefore, when her little daughter had begged a hundred times to play beyond the door yard, when spring had really come and new grass was showing green all over the great sunny plain, she said yes at last. On that morning she and Mary Anne went together down to the creek, to explore the winding banks below which the water sang.

There were patches of snow among the willow trees by the stream, but the sloping meadow was bare and dry. Mary Anne was like a frisky puppy, let loose in the sunshine; she ran and scampered; she danced and sang when the spring wind lifted her hair. Finally she lay down upon the warm slope of the dry grass and rolled, all the way down from the upper edge of the meadow, until she bumped against one of the trees beside the water. Her mother had seated herself on a stone and had taken out her knitting. She did not speak now while Mary Anne sat quiet looking across the plain that, so her father told her, stretched a thousand miles away to meet the mountains. A red-winged blackbird was chuckling and whistling in the tree above her; the water was pouring over the flat ledges of the

creek-bed; tiny fish were darting in the pools between the stones.

It was a beautiful world and, so it seemed, she and her mother had the whole of it to themselves that morning. The two were good comrades. But they could not really play together, for Mrs. Seabold was unendingly busy. She must always be working so that her little household should have wholesome food, a clean house, and warm clothes and stockings. Mary Anne needed one thing more on that bright April day; she needed a playmate of something like her own age.

It seemed as though there were someone else who needed a companion that morning, someone with broader shoulders and longer legs, able to walk a good number of miles in search of a comrade with whom to share the brightness of the warm spring day. As Mary Anne sat beside the willow, she saw a boy walking toward her along the winding bank of the creek.

When he stepped from shade into sunshine, he showed a head of such light yellow hair that it was almost white.

This must be the son of that Norwegian neighbor of whom she had heard her father speak, a farmer who lived five miles beyond the store building. In the blustering winter few visits could be made, so Mary Anne had never seen these nearest white neighbors. But she had heard of them and of their boy, who was some years older than herself. His name, she remembered, was Eric Thorveg.

Mary Anne had always been shy, and she had not become less so in the long months of that lonely winter. Yet the need of a playmate was so great that she did not quite run away when the boy came close, although she could not help slipping out of sight behind the nearest tree. She looked over her shoulder at her mother. Jane Seabold smiled to give her daughter courage, but she did not stop her knitting. She seemed to know well who Eric was and to think that Mary Anne could make friends with him more easily without her help.

The boy seemed not to see her; he drew out a pocket knife, reached above his head, and cut off a branch of willow. With careful, unhurried strokes he trimmed it smooth, shortened it to a few inches long, and seemed to

be cutting a notch in the end. So great was her curiosity
that after a long minute of struggle with her shyness, Mary
Anne came almost all the way around the tree trunk. She
could not understand what he was doing now, for he was
tapping the tiny branch with the handle of his knife. Thus
she observed, as she slipped nearer, that the tapping had
loosened the smooth bark so that it slid off in Eric's hand.
Now he was notching and cutting once more at the inner
wood; then he fitted the bark into its former place and
then, turning to her with a slow smile, he put the finished
toy into her hand.

"Blow it," he directed.

She raised it to her lips, blew once too softly, then, after
drawing a great breath, blew again, a shrill, clear note.
The red-winged blackbird overhead dipped and cocked his
head, as though in wonder that these humans below could
produce a sound so like his own voice.

Mary Anne looked up at Eric with shining eyes. "Oh!"
was all she managed to say.

"It's yours," Eric told her with easy friendliness. "Now
I will make another for myself, and we can call to each
other when I walk down the creek." He cut a new piece
of willow and went on talking as he worked. "I have to
help my father with the cows and the plowing, but there's

time to come over here sometimes. It's lonely at our house."

"At ours too," agreed Mary Anne. She was blowing long and short blasts and found, with practice, that it did not take all her breath. "I'll blow it every day to know if you're coming, every day all summer and all winter too."

"Unless you keep it soaked in water, a willow whistle dries up," Eric explained, "and then it will not sound any more. But you can always make another, whenever you can find a willow tree with a green shoot. See, I'll show you just how."

A good half-hour had passed by the time he had made it clear to her just how the bark was stripped, and had let her try cutting the notch herself. Mrs. Seabold got up and came also to see how a willow whistle was made. She and Eric talked of his father and grandfather, for they were plainly well acquainted. Mary Anne was still too shy to say very much and could only work away at cutting the green wood or watch while Eric, with quick skill, finished the second whistle and blew a loud blast on it. This one was bigger than the first, and had a shriller note. Then he got up from where the two had been sitting together on a twisted root.

"I have to go now," he announced. "It will take me a

long time to get home. But I'll come again. There's no one but big people at our house." He gave them both another friendly smile and set off, trudging steadily away up the creek as though the five miles of tramping across the prairie were no real distance at all.

"We ought to have taken Eric in to eat dinner with us," Jane Seabold said, "but he went away too quickly. No one but big people at his house, did he say? No one at all except his father and his very old grandfather. How lonely the boy must be!"

Eric came again to the playground at the edge of the creek, and yet again. He was not free to be there every day, for his father needed him. So Mary Anne was never quite sure whether she would see him coming along the bank of the stream, as she came running down the path from the house, blowing her willow whistle. She was always happy to hear the note of his in answer, sometimes from where he was waiting under the trees, sometimes from far beyond the bend in the little river. She and her mother came often now to the sloping meadow. They were the owners of a newly hatched flock of lively white turkeys,

which must be driven out as often as possible to run and peck in the fresh grass.

Once, perhaps a week after they had first met, Mary Anne saw Eric beyond the creek, climbing up the bank on the other side. He pointed out where she and Mrs. Seabold could cross the water on stepping-stones, and after Mary Anne had crossed and scrambled up beside him he showed her what he had come across to see. A dun-colored pony, without bridle or halter, was cropping the grass on the levels beyond the creek. He was a slim, graceful creature, with a cream-colored mane and tail that blew out a little in the prairie wind. He stopped grazing and stood looking at them, watchful and alert.

"Is he a wild horse, do you think?" asked Mary Anne. She had heard of the untamed horses that, like the buffalo and the deer, lived in hundreds on the prairie grass.

"Wild horses go in herds," Eric told her. "No, this one must belong to somebody. We'd better catch him."

Catch him, indeed! It seemed as though a swooping pigeon would have been as easy to capture. He wheeled and circled, galloping away the moment they came near,

but never running to any distance. He would stop and wait until they came close, then lope away just out of reach. Mrs. Seabold crossed too and came up the bank to watch and laugh and to admire the quick, clever little horse. His coat was just the dull gray-brown of a deer's, and his slim legs had almost a deer's swiftness.

"I will have him. He's quicker even than Sancho," Eric said. He had told Mary Anne of the yellow pony that his father owned, bought from an Indian for a gun. "You stand still and wave your sunbonnet, so he won't pass you, while I slip up from behind."

Perhaps the pony was tired of the game, for he had stopped to snatch a mouthful of grass, and in that moment Eric had him. The boy caught the cream-colored mane and with one leap was up on the animal's back. Such kicking and bucking, such jumping sideways, such rearing upon dancing hind legs! Eric held his place in spite of every effort to dislodge him, until at last the horse realized that he was captured by a skillful rider, and went sweeping off in a great circle across the grass. He was just dashing up to pass Mary Anne again, with Eric waving his hand in triumph, when a strange, clear call came from beside the river. A tall Indian came into view above the bank some yards upstream. At his summons the dun pony swung about so abruptly that Eric went sprawling headlong to fall unhurt upon the soft grass. The Indian said no word to the two white children who were apparently trying to steal his horse, but swung himself up on the pony's back with a movement as easy as a lifting bird's, and galloped away. He had come and gone so quickly that not even Jane Seabold had found time to be frightened.

Two days later, when Mary Anne came across the meadow to look for Eric, she saw to her surprise that the Indian had come back, that he had turned the pony out to graze and was talking to the boy, that is, if talk can be carried on by half a dozen English words, a few grunts, and a good many signs. The girl looked back anxiously at her mother, who was bringing the cheeping white turkeys down the path. Jane Seabold stopped for a minute, scarcely knowing whether she ought to be afraid or not. In the end she seemed to remember her husband's words about the friendliness of the Indians, and she came slowly forward. The boy seemed to be telling his friend who Mary Anne and her mother were, for the stranger nodded and made a gesture with both hands, like someone balancing a pair of scales. That was to show that he knew they were the wife and daughter of the man who kept the trading post, who weighed out powder and salt in exchange for furs.

The red-skinned newcomer seated himself upon a boulder beside the stream and remained there so long and so still

that presently the others almost forgot his presence. Jane Seabold was busy knitting again, and the two children, when they were not driving back the straying turkeys, were soon deep in the games that they loved to play. Mrs. Seabold's needles clicked as busily as ever, while Eric and Mary Anne ran and romped across the meadow as though the tall, quiet man were not there.

After that he came often, seeming to have formed some strange, silent friendship for the boy who had been able to ride his horse and for the little girl and her mother who were not afraid of him. He did not belong to any of the nearby villages, they learned presently, but had traveled from very far away. His name was Gray Eagle, and from the number of feathers in his hair they knew he was a chief. He would ride up to the door of the trading house, too, dismount from the dun pony, and come striding in. Sometimes he brought a few furs to trade, sometimes he came empty-handed, to sit and watch the white man carry on business with his own red kinsmen. He never went home again without coming first to the playground under the willow trees to watch Eric and Mary Anne at their

games. To them alone he would sometimes talk by means of his vivid signs and his half-dozen words of English. The boy, the girl, and her mother began to watch for his silent presence, then to feel well acquainted with him; and at last they grew truly fond of him.

Spring had almost turned to summer, and the willows were in full leaf. The turkeys were growing long-legged and awkward and were beginning to try to preen and strut just as the old ones did. They could run more quickly now, and seemed more and more determined to stray away, to lose themselves, or let themselves be caught by some watchful hawk. Turkeys are difficult to bring up and seem to delight in running to meet danger.

One afternoon, as Mary Anne came down the slope of the meadow she noticed that the shadows below the trees were very long. It was later than she had thought, perhaps too late to find Eric there. She had been helping to make wild-strawberry jam, a task that was only just ended. Her mother was following some distance behind, with the turkeys spread all across the grass between them.

She stood looking up the creek bed to watch whether her

playmate might be coming, but she saw no one, and in a moment she was startled by a sudden growl of thunder almost overhead. A heavy rain-cloud was rolling up from the west. Mary Anne had grown used to such sudden storms, and she rather liked the great gusts of warm wind and the downpour of cooling rain with the sunshine following so quickly afterward. She knew, however, that rain was dangerous for little turkeys, who are apt to die if they once get thoroughly wet.

At the first real thunderclap the silly, frightened fowls scattered in a dozen directions, running in among the willows, through the tall weeds—anywhere except toward home.

"Quick, Mary Anne!" her mother called. "Get those five who have run so far and drive them to the house the shortest way!" A few of the frantic little birds had scurried away along the edge of the stream and would soon be out of sight beyond a distant bend.

Mary Anne ran after them, but they raced far ahead and disappeared. She followed, quick-footed, around the curving bank, and then stopped suddenly, for someone was sitting at the foot of a big willow, apparently waiting. Wrapped in his scarlet blanket, Gray Eagle was seated on a fallen log, watching her as she came toward him through the trees. She was glad to see him; perhaps he would help her to find the turkeys, which by this time were nowhere to be seen. Gray Eagle spoke a single word as she came near.

"Eric?" he said.

He was asking a question; he wished to know where the boy was. She shook her head. Very probably Eric was at home, as busy as she had been, but there was no way in which she could tell him that. He was staring at her very

intently. He had never really smiled, but when he looked
at either of his two young friends his face always had a
look of quiet kindness. Mary Anne had heard that Indians
were gentle with their own children, and were equally
good to those of other people if they liked them. He sat
for a long time and then suddenly got up and held out
his hand.

"Come," he said. It was an English word that he had
never used before. Perhaps, Mary Anne thought, he had
learned it just to say to her. For the first time since she
had known him she saw him smile. She hesitated, her
eyes raised to his. The rain was falling now but very little
was touching her as she stood below the thick branches of
the willow tree. The look on Gray Eagle's face seemed
to say, "Do you doubt me?"

She did not; she was sure that whatever he meant, it was
not to do her harm. She let him lead her down to the edge
of the water. The deer-colored pony was nibbling the
grass close by, this time with a rawhide rope trailing from
his neck to keep him from straying. The Indian called him,
lifted Mary Anne upon the horse's back, and jumped up

behind her. Mary Anne thought that he was taking her home, but no, he turned the pony's head to the creek and went splashing through the ford.

"But—but where are we going?" she cried.

The storm was already clearing. She had caught a glimpse of her mother, driving the excited turkeys with great difficulty up to their door. Jane Seabold must have thought that Mary Anne had got home before her, for she did not look back.

The Indian did not answer Mary Anne's question, but he regarded her with that fixed, friendly look which somehow made it impossible for her to be afraid. She pointed toward home, then pointed toward the sun, visible through a space in the breaking clouds, and now dropping so low that the wide, empty plain would soon be dark. He only shook his head and spoke to the pony. The little horse stretched himself to a long, smooth lope that carried them steadily away across the broad prairie.

THE SEARCH PARTY

Eric Thorveg had been told by his friend the Indian chief to be at the playground beside the creek just when the sun had dropped to the level of the willow tops. Because his grandfather had needed his help, the boy was late. Even though he ran a great part of the way and never thought of turning back when the rain began, he did not reach the stream until the storm had almost passed and the round red sun had just touched the edge of the prairie. There was no Chief Gray Eagle, no yellow-maned pony, and no playmate, Mary Anne.

He looked all about him and saw, far across the rolling grass, a black dot disappearing to the westward, a moving horse with a blanketed rider. Surely there was someone else on the horse, held in front of the Indian? Gray Eagle had carried Mary Anne away with him! Eric ran some distance after them and called with all his strength, "Gray Eagle! Mary Anne!" The soft west wind, rippling the half-grown grass, carried his voice back. There was no hope that he could be heard by the distant rider, who never looked behind him.

"Now," thought Eric, still in something of a daze, "I must go up to the cabin and tell Mary Anne's mother."

He turned into the path Mary Anne's feet had trodden deep in the meadow grass. He had run so far and in such haste that his legs ached and felt a little shaky. He walked slower and slower and when he was halfway to the Seabold cottage he stopped entirely and sat down on the green slope to think a minute. He must tell Mrs. Seabold what Gray Eagle had done; he must explain to her that there was no reason for being frightened. But what was he to say?

Indians have strange ways, such strange ways that white

men come to understand them very slowly. In some respects the red men are more like children than grown people, so that it might easily be that a boy could take in their ideas more readily than a man or a woman. Eric, walking and talking every day with his good friend Gray Eagle, even though each could understand so little of the other's language, had got to know something of the red men's habits and ways of thinking.

Gray Eagle had dropped words now and then of a way he and his comrades·had of showing their friendship for a white man whom they had come to trust. It was to take the white man's children to their camp for a visit, keep them for seven days, and then bring them home again. The Indian would say nothing of his plan—he would simply take the children away and later return them. The white man also was supposed to say nothing; he was to show his trust in the Indian by waiting without question—if he could— until the children came home. Thus a friendship was to be pledged that was to last forever.

Gray Eagle had even let fall more than one hint that such a thing might happen some day to Eric and Mary Anne. Evidently, when he had told the boy to be at the bend of the creek at sunset, it must have meant that this

was the moment when the plan was to be carried out. But Eric had been delayed and the Sioux had gone with Mary Anne alone. Eric got up from the grass at last and went along the path. It was all so clear to him that surely he could explain it to Mary Anne's mother.

Mrs. Seabold was busy inside, but she had come to the door more than once to look for her little daughter. She was not concerned, even now. Perhaps she was thinking that Mary Anne had stopped under the shelter of the willow trees until the rain was entirely over. It was Eric who came up the path instead, to stand upon the doorstone and speak in a steady voice, so that she need not take alarm.

Jane Seabold was a brave woman. Women who were real cowards did not come to the prairie country to live. She turned white when Eric got out his first stuttering news that her little daughter was gone, but she listened quietly to all he had to say. John Seabold came in before the boy had finished and stood hearkening also.

"I thought something like that might be going to happen," he said, when Eric stopped speaking. "Well, we can only wait. To try to go after her would only do harm. The Indians would never let us find her, and besides, they would be angry. Just keep steady, Mother, she'll come back in a week."

Seven days can be very long when three people are watching every hour ticked off by the big clock in the corner of the cabin. Eric would wake up in the night and count the days over again, to make sure that he had not lost his reckoning. He would wonder, for the hundredth time, what Mary Anne was doing and thinking. Was she sound asleep on buffalo skins beside a smoldering campfire, or was she awake, staring up at the pointed roof of the lodge and thinking about Eric, as he was thinking about her?

The seventh day came. Eric sat on the creek bank from morning until late afternoon, watching the wide, empty prairie for some sign of a loping horse bringing Gray Eagle and Mary Anne home again. Mrs. Seabold came to the cabin door a hundred times and stood shading her eyes with her hand, to catch the first glimpse of anything moving on that great stretch of green. John Seabold went to his store in the morning as usual, but he was back in an hour, walking uneasily from the cabin to the creek and back again. By the middle of the afternoon Eric's father and his grandfather had ridden over from their farm and had brought with them two Indians from the nearest village. They all stood watching together as the sun went down— and no one came. John Seabold went into the shed behind the house and brought out two saddled horses.

"There's no need to be afraid, even yet," he declared stoutly. "But we—we'll ride out to meet them."

Grandfather Thorveg, it was arranged, would stay behind with Mrs. Seabold. "Is the boy to go?" the old man asked doubtfully.

"We need him," John Seabold returned shortly. "I think he knows more about these Indians than we do."

They rode forward—two men, two Indians, and a boy— without talking, as the sun went down, as the darkness spread over the prairie, then as the moon came up behind them and lighted the whole silent world with her cold shining. Coyotes barked, a deer stamped in the brush as they crossed a creek, a big, soft-winged owl swooped past them, almost brushing Eric's shoulder.

"Do you know how far it is to Gray Eagle's village?" John Seabold asked one of the Indians at last. The red rider pointed to the moon now high overhead, then waved his hand toward the sky to the westward. He meant that the moon would be well down toward the horizon before they came to the wide river beside which Gray Eagle's clan had set up their lodges. John Seabold nodded and pressed on, the others trailing out behind him.

The ground over which they were riding finally began to be quite unfamiliar. Instead of the smooth grass, there were little stony ridges, with groups of low trees between them, and small bushy thickets. Far to the north of them they could see, in the moonlight, a line of low hills.

"There's the gap where the river runs through," said Eric's father, pointing. "We can't be many miles from the village now. But I don't see any campfires."

Eric was riding the yellow pony Sancho, which was known to be both swift and lazy. The little animal liked racing, but this long steady gallop was not to his taste. He lagged behind the other horses and was beginning to pay less and less attention to his rider's efforts to make him hurry. He and Eric finally got so far in the rear that the four men ahead disappeared over the crest of a ridge, up whose slope the loafing Sancho refused to climb with any haste.

As he looked away to the right to see if the climb might be less steep somewhere else, Eric was surprised to see a small light moving and dancing among some stunted trees not far away. Scarcely thinking what he was doing, the

boy turned the pony's head to ride nearer and see what this darting glint of fire might be. It bobbed back and forth as he came closer but did not move away. Yet he could not come quite up to it, for Sancho was presently halted by a steep, narrow creek-bed so full of deep, black shadows that it would have been madness indeed to plunge into it in the uncertain light. The moon, however, made it clear enough that on the opposite bank there was a horse with a rider mounted—an Indian so light and slim that he was surely a boy no older than Eric. He carried a burning torch, a light that flickered in the wind, then burned anew as he swung it around his head.

"Hey—yah!" he called, and whirled his horse about to stand even with Eric's, while the stream ran between. There was challenge in the call, the challenge to a race, as even Sancho knew at once. He had been an Indian's pony before the elder Thorveg had bought him for a gun, and he had run many races, for racing is the sport that Indians love best.

Down the little valley the two horses and the two riders went thundering, first the Indian ahead, then the white

boy. There were rocks and stumps and hidden hollows in the way, but these were heeded by neither boys nor ponies. The stream grew narrower as the chasm deepened, so that the two came closer and closer together in their headlong race. Again and again the Indian shouted aloud to his horse to urge him forward, while Eric only spoke low— "On, Sancho! Get on and pass him!"

They were neck and neck, then the Indian was drawing ahead. Sancho was on his mettle now that he was in danger of being beaten, and stretched to the contest with no further urging. Slowly, slowly Eric came up level with the other, only a few yards away now, with the deep-running creek splashing between and the thunder of the racing feet sounding hollow along the bank. Then suddenly the Indian checked his pony, jerking it back upon its haunches, as he lifted his torch high and shouted with one last defiant yell. The flame streamed out like a banner and showed the rider in full light, a boy, as Eric thought, no bigger than himself, with streaming black hair and a scarlet band around his head.

Eric saw him for an instant, then felt his own pony lurch

forward, and heard the sliding sound of earth and stones
giving way under the four plunging feet. They had come
to a high bank where the small stream cut through to fall
into the bigger river. The Indian had pulled up just in
time, but Eric and Sancho went scrambling and tumbling
over into the black darkness below. They fell, horse and
rider at some distance from each other, upon a soft bank
of sand, then got up, both of them dizzy and trembling but
neither of them injured.

"Good gracious, boy, where did you drop from?" said
John Seabold's voice close by. The four men had been
riding up the shore of the river and had stopped, startled,
as Eric and his mount came shooting over the moon-lighted
bank to fall almost at their feet.

The two Indians did not speak at once. They were
looking up at the red-skinned boy with his torch, on the
ridge above. The wild rider, with one last whoop of
mocking defiance, wheeled and galloped away.

"No Sioux," said the Indian nearest Eric. And the other
added—"Arickaree, not friend."

His few words of English could not tell them much, but
it made them understand vaguely that something must
surely be wrong. The Arickaree Indians were neighbors

of the Sioux but were unfriendly to them. Each tribe was
fond of attacking the other's villages, trying to scatter and
drive away their horses, for horses are the property that
Indians prize the most. The whole party rode forward
quickly, though the only further words were spoken by
John Seabold:

"Gray Eagle's village should be just there, at the bend of
the river."

They came to the place where the river swept in a great
curve, shining in the moonlight. Here indeed had been the
Indian camp; there were marks of horses' feet everywhere,
piles of embers where fires had been hastily trodden out,
tumbled heaps of skins where lodges had been knocked
down. But there was never a voice or a sound, not a shelter
standing, not a grazing horse or a barking dog to show that
a band of Indians had lived here for months past. The
white riders stood still, staring blankly about them.

"I see what has happened," said Eric's father. "The
Arickarees came riding down to drive away the Sioux horses.
Gray Eagle's men knew there were too many for them to
fight, so they just scattered and slipped away. There has
been no battle here—the Sioux got away too quickly. When
Indians decide not to make a fight, they can disappear like

a broken covey of quail. There's no knowing where they've gone."

There was no need for anyone to add, "And there is no knowing what has happened to Mary Anne."

"You ride up the river bank," John Seabold directed Eric's father, and then pointed, so that each Indian should know where he was to go. He turned about to tell Eric to keep with one of the older riders. But the boy had already been taken with a plan of his own. He had chosen the trail leading from the shore toward the hills, had swung Sancho up the bank, and had disappeared among the shadows.

WITH THE INDIANS

Mary Anne rode away on the loping pony, carried in front of Chief Gray Eagle, but she understood well that there was no danger before her, only some pleasant and exciting adventure. Eric had told her a little of what the Sioux had said of a custom among the Indians of sometimes taking white children to visit their villages. She looked up at Gray Eagle and knew that the puckers still visible on his leathery, red-brown face were meant for an Indian's smile.

If he had been a stranger she would have understood very clearly that she should never let him entice her away. She would have struggled and fought, and called for help until someone heard her in the cabin beyond the creek. But Gray Eagle was a friend of many weeks' standing. John Seabold, Mary Anne's father, liked and respected him; even her mother had lost her fear of him. She had heard her father say that the friendship of Gray Eagle and his people would mean much to the prosperity of the trade in the log store building. There was one thing, however, that must be settled. Mary Anne pointed once more back toward the cabin, and asked a question she hoped Gray Eagle would understand.

"My mother—what will she think?"

His smile grew a very little broader.

"White squaw understand—not afraid."

Did he know perhaps that Eric, or that someone, would explain to Jane Seabold this strange custom that the Indians had, of carrying away a white man's children to try whether the white man would trust them?

It grew so dark presently that she could no longer see

Gray Eagle's face. They rode so far and so late that finally she fell asleep, with her head against his gay blanket.

She never knew, therefore, how far they had traveled before she was aroused suddenly by voices all about her and a glare of red fires in her eyes. The pony had stopped at last, in the midst of an Indian village much like the very small ones nearer to the cabin at home. But here were strange faces all about her, chattering squaws, peering, brown-faced children whom she had never seen before. The rows of campfires lit up the long lines of pointed lodges, showing a far larger settlement than any that she knew. She was still blinking and drowsy when a squaw lifted her down from the pony, carried her through the gaping black door of the nearest wigwam, and laid her upon a soft bed of buffalo robes, where in a moment she was asleep again.

It was startling to wake in the morning, look about in that strange place, and wonder how she came to be there. But there was breakfast of roast partridge and buffalo steak to be eaten; there was a crowd of wondering, small brown faces peering past the deerhide curtain of the lodge door. All the children in Gray Eagle's village had hurried there to stare at the marvel of a white child come to visit and to play with them.

When Mary Anne finally came running out, however, they seemed to forget that she was different, and to accept her as one of themselves. One or two stroked her gingham dress with curious fingers, and then felt of their own

scanty garments of tanned leather, as though wondering how there could be such a difference. Some bold ones even touched her bright, soft hair, so oddly unlike their own rough black locks. But most of them seemed to waste little thought upon the strangeness of her white skin and her blue checked dress, but fell to teaching her how to play their games of ball or showing her their ponies, brown and black, pinto and dapple-gray. The horses were grazing in a great scattered herd all about the group of lodges, for Gray Eagle's village, while it contained no very vast number of people, was very rich in Indian wealth, which is counted by the number of horses each family owns.

Every morning Mary Anne thought, "My father will come for me today." When evening came she would go to sleep thinking drowsily, "Surely he and Eric will come tomorrow."

She was not homesick, for there were too many new and exciting things to see and to do. It had happened several times that her father and mother had had to make the long journey to the nearest white man's town on business and for supplies. Then they had taken her to the house of one neighbor or another to stay until they came back, so she was used to being away from home without wondering too much or asking questions.

Her gingham dress was torn by the thorn bushes through which she ran and raced, playing ball with her new comrades. Gray Eagle's mother, Swift Pigeon, the gentle-faced old squaw who cared for his lodge, gave her a new dress of soft white deerskin, with fringes and porcupine-

quill embroideries. Her stout shoes seemed hard and clumsy beside the soft moccasins of the other children, so Swift Pigeon made her a pair for herself, with round, puckered toes and bright beads around the ankles. Her hair was bound with a red-embroidered leather band holding two wild-goose feathers. She had a pony of her own, a kind-hearted old rusty-brown fellow, who could canter as fast as the rest, but who did not jump and buck as the others did.

Mary Anne rode him at full gallop along the dusty trails worn in the grass; she ran races with the girls her own size; she plunged and tumbled after the deerhide ball, or watched the older children play the game of plum stones. There was little except her yellow hair to show that she was not an Indian.

A day arrived when the whole camp was full of talk and laughter and a great bustle of getting ready for something. That evening, so she was made to understand, the village was to hold its spring festival, the Dance of the Omahas. At this time all the babies who had been born within the year were to be given their names.

Everyone must help to get ready. A great space was cleared and made smooth just beyond the edge of the village. All the children, large and small, helped to bring wood for the circle of fires that were to be lighted and kept burning all around the open ground where the dancing was to be.

It was just at sunset that the dance began. Every squaw came out of her lodge wearing all her beads, her chains of elks' teeth and of bears' claws. Every brave had his most splendid war-bonnet of eagle quills, red, yellow, and blue, his lance with its swinging ornaments of colored feathers, and his bow and arrows in a decorated quiver. The babies all lay upon the grass together at the center of the circle, wrapped in their gayest and most carefully embroidered coverings. The skin drums thumped, the gourd rattles sounded, the tall warriors went round and round them in a

great circle, dancing their strange, slow, stamping shuffle and calling the long *Ah*-ha-ha, *Ah*-ha-ha, of their solemn chant. The medicine man, with his jingling necklaces and dangling charms and his headdress of buffalo horns, would take up one child after another and give it a name. The little thing would stare and blink at him and never make a sound. Indian babies seemed to learn very early that they must not cry, Mary Anne said to herself.

Then the swinging dance began again. The sky grew very dark and the stars came out. Beyond the dancers, the horses had scattered far over the plain to graze. Sometimes in a pause of the chanting and the thumping of the drums Mary Anne could hear a pony stamping or whinnying in the shadows. She leaned her head against Swift Pigeon's knee and the dancing circle seemed to swing farther and farther away as her heavy eyelids drooped lower and lower.

Then suddenly there was a ringing shout, a stamping of thundering hoofs, and a great outcry going up all about her.

Was it part of the dance, she wondered? But no, it could not be! Horses were charging across the open ground, scattering the fires, knocking the drums and the dancers in all directions. She could hear Gray Eagle calling orders to his warriors. It was by his command, probably, that the flaming firebrands were stamped out and the whole yelling confusion was plunged into darkness.

Mary Anne felt Swift Pigeon's strong, lean old arm gather her up. The little girl knew dimly that the squaw had also snatched up a baby from the ground, that she had caught the mane of a plunging pony, and had somehow got the three of them—Mary Anne, the papoose, and herself—up on its back. Then they were galloping away into the black emptiness of the prairie, and the shouting grew faint and far away behind them.

"What is it? What happened?" Mary Anne had to ask more than once before the old woman answered in one word—"Arickarees."

She remembered hearing from her playmates that the powerful Arickaree Indians were the enemies of her friends the Sioux, and that they sometimes came in great bands, swooping down upon the village like hawks, to steal the Sioux horses. Were they fighting there behind her in the dark, she wondered? Would Gray Eagle and her playfellows be hurt? She managed to make Swift Pigeon understand her question and received the reply.

"No, too many."

When Indians are attacked by too great a force of the enemy, they are always wise enough to run away, to scatter like blown leaves in a thousand directions. Thus, Gray Eagle, with his people and his horses, had vanished into the dark, just as they had done a hundred times before. If any of their ponies were captured by the Arickarees, they would be certain to get them back some day, by just the same kind of surprise attack in the night.

It was the yellow-maned horse with the fleet legs and the coat the color of a deer that Swift Pigeon had caught in the dark. She urged him on and on, so far finally that his quick feet began to go unevenly on rough ground, and Mary Anne began to see low hills all about them, rising up against the starry sky. They were in strange country, farther away from the village than Mary Anne had ever ridden. She began to think that they had traveled so far that no one, friend or enemy, would be able to follow and find them.

ERIC HEARS A WILLOW WHISTLE

When Eric swung away from the deserted camp beside the river and turned his pony's head toward the hills, he knew exactly why he chose that special direction. The men were looking for the vanished Sioux Indians and the lost little girl all across the great plain to the west and south. Why did the boy seek to find her in the broken country toward the north? This was what he was thinking, if his thoughts had been put into words:

"Gray Eagle carried Mary Anne away because he was a friend, not an enemy. So when he and his people ran away from the Arickaree horse thieves they would take Mary Anne to the very safest place they knew."

And where would she be more securely hidden than in those broken hills just showing in the faint starlight so far away to the north? Sancho was tired, but he seemed to have forgotten his laziness for the time being, and to know as well as his rider that theirs was a pressing errand. He stretched his weary legs to the new trail and loped forward.

The sun came up and showed them the way more plainly, though the hills seemed no nearer. It was one of those hot, heavy days that come at the beginning of summer. They stopped as they crossed a shallow-running creek, and both of them drank. Eric munched some bread and cheese that his grandfather had slipped into his pocket before he set out. Sancho cropped a few mouthfuls of grass and would have liked to linger, but went on obediently when Eric slid into the saddle once more.

By noon they had reached uneven, barren country where the edge of the great grassy plain had just begun to break up into cracks and ravines. The sun was fiercely hot overhead and the sky was without a cloud. Both boy and

355

pony were so worn out that it was plain they must rest a little before they could possibly go forward. They came to a wide creek-bed, so nearly empty of water that it held only a series of pools instead of a running stream. Its course bent around a broad sandy curve where grew a dense and tangled thicket of young poplar trees.

It was the trees that decided Eric to stop here to eat, drink, and rest. Any patch of shade looked welcome indeed after the blinding brightness of the beating sun. He guided Sancho carefully down the steep bank into the sandy bottom lands, skirted the poplar grove—and stopped short.

A vast, shaggy beast came splashing and snorting through the shallow water and out on the sand. It was a great bull buffalo, big-shouldered and heavy-horned, with the shaft of an Indian arrow standing out from a wound in his neck. An ordinary grazing buffalo is fairly peaceable, but a wounded bull is a bellowing whirlwind of stupid rage. The moment his glinting eyes caught sight of Eric and the tired pony, he dropped his horns and charged at them.

Swiftly Sancho fled along the sandy level, keeping close to the poplar thicket. An angry buffalo can gallop faster than a tired pony, but this buffalo was fortunately floundering in the heavy sand. How long he had carried that tormenting arrow in his shoulder Eric could not know. It was only plain to him that the great beast knew that a human hunter had hurt him, and that now he was going to hurt someone in his turn.

356

They rounded the end of the poplar grove and Eric saw the steep bank rise before him. The worn-out pony could never scramble up it, not even when he was driven by terror of the furious animal at his heels. There was nothing to do but swing about, still skirting the edge of the poplars, and ride in a wide curve down toward the stream again.

The buffalo's big clumsy feet had stumbled and sunk deeper in the sand than Eric had thought. Snorting and angry, their pursuer was still following them, but more and more slowly. The boy and the pony had come in a circle all the way around the grove of trees and had galloped so much faster than the buffalo that they were now behind him instead of in front. Eric was breathless and knew that they were still in danger, but in spite of that he almost laughed aloud.

A buffalo viewed from behind is very different from a buffalo seen from in front. When one looks at his huge shoulders, at the hump behind them covered with a shaggy mane of hair, at his heavy head and short thick horns, he seems a terrible beast indeed. But observed from the rear, he shows a sloping back and such small hind legs that he does not seem terrible at all, but even a little ridiculous.

At the sound of the horse's hoofs behind him, the big bull did not wheel about, but only struggled harder and harder to plunge forward through the sand. The hunter whose arrow had wounded his shoulder had shot him from the rear and now, in his dull buffalo mind, the big creature could only think that he was being pursued again. He snorted with terror, though a minute before he had been bellowing with rage. Eric shouted, to drive him still faster. With a scramble of hasty hoofs and a rattle of stones all about him, the great beast went climbing up the bank to the level above. The arrow caught on a branch of poplar and was jerked free. In wonder and relief but still in a tremendous fright, the buffalo, with his head lowered and his tail straight up in the air, went galloping away across the plain and disappeared.

Eric slipped out of the saddle, sat down on the sand, and drew a long breath. The pony wasted no time in wondering over their escape but waded into the water and dropped his head to take a long cool drink. All about them the sand was torn and trampled by those clumsy cloven feet, but the danger was safely past. Eric loosened the cinch on Sancho's saddle, and lifted the saddle off. The grateful pony scrambled up the bank to the green level above and rolled gloriously on the soft grass. Then he fell to snatching a hasty dinner, while Eric lay at full length on the sand in the shade of the poplars, closed his eyes, and listened to the whispering of the lightly hung leaves and the comfortable

358

munching of Sancho on the bank above his head. He must go on in a few minutes to look for Mary Anne, but he knew enough to keep lazily quiet and to rest completely as he lay for that short time upon the sand. Sancho came obediently at his whistle when it was necessary to saddle and ride on once more.

Eric traveled more slowly now, looking anxiously at the ground as he rode. If any of the Sioux Indians had come this way bringing Mary Anne, he might, with good luck, catch sight of the trail left by their horses. Wherever there was soft ground near a watercourse, wherever the fresh grass had been newly trampled or the branches of a willow thicket had been recently broken, there were plenty of footprints of animals, large and small. There he drew rein and studied the marks of buffalo and the marks of the small, sharp hoofs of deer and antelope. The bent and broken twigs among the willows showed where a buck deer had slept the night before and—perhaps startled by some unfamiliar sound—had jumped up and gone crashing away through the low, tangled branches. But of the traces of horses' feet he found none.

It was late afternoon when they mounted the first slope that brought them into the hill country. All about them ran little streams in beds so narrow that they seemed like deep cracks cut between the rocky ridges. Eric stopped his pony and stood wondering and hesitating on the crest of the first ridge. It would take hours to explore even one of the creeks, and there were a dozen to choose from. And in not more than two hours it would be dark. Which way should he go? Sancho settled the question by half sliding, half cantering down the nearest slope toward the largest pool that they had yet seen. He was thirsty and cool water was near; that was enough. As Eric sat waiting for him to lift his head from his luxurious drinking, the boy saw plainly in the soft earth beside them the trampled print of hoofs. This time they were not deer or buffalo tracks; they were the marks of the unshod feet of an Indian pony. He interrupted his horse's gulping with an abrupt jerk of the reins.

"Go on, Sancho!" he ordered, in fierce excitement.

The creek wound and twisted in and out among the hills. Eric followed it mile after mile, looking, listening, getting down now and again as the shadows grew deeper to examine the wet margin of the stream. Once, then again, he found new footprints; he was going in the right direction. At every turn of the crooked way he would think, "Now, I will find them!" But each new stretch of the narrow valley was as empty as the last.

The ravine broadened finally to a green, grassy bowl, wide enough to catch a gleam from the dropping sun. A spur of rocks ran down from the ridge almost to the edge of the water, but all the rest of the hillside was smooth and covered with close-growing sod. The stream wound through the level space at the bottom, its banks covered with fresh, green willows. Eric and Sancho stood still and looked and looked.

Was that a faint curl of smoke going up from beyond the rocks? It was so thin and transparent that he could not be sure. Was that an animal moving up the far slope of the valley? Was it a deer grazing—or a pony with a deer-colored coat? And if it was a pony, if that was the smoke of a burned-out campfire, to whom did both belong? To friendly Sioux Indians, or to hostile Arickarees? How could he know?

A little breeze stirred the willows. Something moved close to the green bank, something showing a glint of red. Then, drifting softly on the wind, there came a thin, wavering sound, a high, shrill piping. No Indian could have cut and fashioned a green whistle that would blow just that note. There was no one who knew how, except the friend and playmate whom he had come so far to seek.

"Mary Anne!" he shouted with all his might, and in answer the sound came again, the clear call of a willow whistle.

ESCAPE AND RETURN

As Mary Anne came rushing to meet Eric across the little grassy valley, her first words were a warning.

"Crouch down, here under the bushes! Swift Pigeon said I must never run across the open grass like that, but—but when I saw you—"

She did not finish. Her shining face was enough to tell her comrade just how welcome he was.

"Why must we hide?" he said, but she hushed him instantly.

"Not so loud! Speak in a whisper. The—the Arickarees might hear us."

Eric crouched obediently, stole down to the edge of the water, and hid himself beside her under the drooping cover of the scrub alders. He listened silently while Mary Anne, speaking low and close to his ear, gave him the whole account of her adventures in the Sioux village and of the flight with Swift Pigeon, the brown baby, and the dun pony, when the Arickaree Indians scattered her friends in the dark.

"Swift Pigeon will hardly let me get out of her sight. We

build the littlest fires there behind the rocks, and we eat berries and fish, and try to keep hidden all the time. She thinks the Arickarees may find us yet."

She looked anxiously all about them, and crept even deeper under the bushes. There was no sound or sight of anyone behind the spur of jutting boulders, and the little curl of smoke had floated quite away. Eric touched the green whistle she still held in her hand.

"And where did you get that?" he asked. "The old one must have dried up long ago."

"I got so tired of sitting still below the rock," she answered, "so I slipped down to the water and I was thinking so much about the cabin at home and about you, that before I knew it I was cutting myself a willow whistle just the way you showed me. And then I heard a horse's feet and saw you and Sancho come over the ridge, and if there had been a thousand Arickaree Indians listening, I couldn't have helped blowing the whistle to make you hear!"

Eric, falling under the spell of her whispering anxiety, stole out from the thicket, unsaddled his pony, and hid the saddle and bridle behind a log. He drove Sancho up the

363

slope to graze out of sight beyond a stretch of brushy trees, and then came back to his place beside Mary Anne. But he was not quite sure that they really had to take such care to keep hidden.

"Gray Eagle's village is miles and miles away," he said. "The Arickarees only wanted the horses, and certainly they would never follow you so far just to get one more."

"They all wanted our pony; the Indians everywhere for miles around had heard of Gray Eagle's horse that runs so fast and is the color of a deer. Swift Pigeon knew the Arickarees would ride and ride until they found him. She chose the way so carefully as we came along, always going on hard ground so the pony's feet would not leave a mark. Now and then we had to cross a river where the bank was soft, but she wouldn't let me get down for fear of making footprints."

Eric had taken no such care—he had found them on a chance guess. But would anyone following his trail need to trust to good fortune? That trail was marked as clear as noonday the whole of the way. Had anyone been riding behind him?

"Do you think—" he began. Mary Anne put her hand on his arm to silence him.

She had been hiding in that place only two days and a night, but the sense of danger had already taught her ears to be very keen. In a minute Eric heard the sound she had caught first, the noise of scrambling and trampling feet. A horse and rider came over the ridge that Eric had crossed and stood just where he had first stopped, looking all across the valley. It had grown darker now, for it was more than an hour later, but it was still light enough to show the lean, long-legged horse and the tall rider with feathers in his hair. It was an Indian—an enemy Arickaree and not a friendly

Sioux. And as the horse crossed the ridge in the last of the clear light, Eric knew even what Arickaree it was—that boy of his own age who had swung his torch and challenged him to a race above the river bank.

The two under the bushes hardly dared breathe as the Indian came near. He rode by, so close that when his horse's hoof struck a rotten log the splinters flew into Mary Anne's lap. She did not move a muscle. Swift Pigeon had taught her what every Indian woman teaches every Indian child, what every mother deer, rabbit, and partridge teaches her babies—that to keep absolutely still is far safer than to run away.

Somewhere behind the spur of ragged stones, the old Indian woman, Swift Pigeon, was clasping the brown baby and crouching, equally motionless and watchful, while their enemy rode by without seeing them.

An older brave would have looked to right and left, would have noticed a dislodged stone or a blowing, half-burned leaf that turned over and over before the fluttering evening breeze. But the Arickaree lad saw nothing save the prize that he had come so far to seek—the dun pony. Gray Eagle's horse had grazed out on the open slope and was plainly visible even in the fading light. His head was up, his pale mane was blowing. Through his wide nostrils came a snort of angry defiance. Indian ponies are wise little beasts; among other things they catch easily the difference between a friend and an enemy.

There followed a contest so intense and exciting that the two in the bushes could hardly even pretend to hide themselves, so eager were they to see what was to happen. The clever Sioux pony doubled and dodged, ran headlong, then stopped short to spin about and speed away in the opposite direction. He never lost his footing on the steep

slope, and he stayed in the open ground away from the
rocks and wooded hillside, where he could wheel and
scamper without hindrance.

The long-legged Arickaree horse was no match for him
in agility or speed. He tried to follow and turn as the dun
pony did, but he was clumsy and slow beside that other,
whose quickness was like a darting swallow's. Under his
rider's beating quirt, the bigger mount lumbered heavily up
and down in pursuit, but was always left far behind in the
game of catch-as-catch-can.

"He will never get him!" rejoiced Mary Anne, but Eric
shook his head.

"The Arickaree has something more than just his horse.
Look!"

The Indian rider was uncoiling the rawhide rope that
hung at his horse's withers. He tested the smooth-running
noose at the end, whirled it about his head, and flung it as
the pony sped by. The little beast was quick and clever,

but man's wit was too much for him. The noose dropped about his neck, and he stopped short in a sliding plunge, making one last attempt to throw the rope over his head. It settled and tightened about his neck—and he was fairly caught. The Arickaree boy leaped to the ground and swung himself up on the back of his prize.

"The pony will throw him just the way he threw you," Mary Anne said to Eric.

But she was mistaken. Gray Eagle's swift horse, who had bucked Eric over his head with such cheerful ease, now submitted sullenly, and stood with hanging head while his new master took a turn of the rope around the little horse's lower jaw—the Indian substitute for a bridle. Then they rode away, all three of them, the stranger, the meek captured pony, and the long-legged horse, trailing in the rear. The big tears were rolling down Mary Anne's cheeks as she saw them go. Her grief was only over the loss of a good friend; she was not thinking of any further trouble until Eric said:

"It's not going to be very easy to get home now."

Worn-out Sancho was their only mount, and he had been ridden for a night and a day. He could go no farther without at least a day of rest. Then he could carry Swift Pigeon, Mary Anne, and the papoose, while Eric must walk beside them for all of that long, slow journey through country where the enemy was still at large.

"Perhaps your father or mine will find us before we've got very far," he reassured Mary Anne, but he had no very hopeful heart behind the words. It was a boy's guess to try riding in the direction he had taken, a lucky guess, for he had found Mary Anne. But with something of a boy's carelessness he had neglected to tell any of his companions which way he was going. And there were many miles of prairie and hills to be searched before John Seabold might chance to follow him.

When Mary Anne brought Eric to the little camp under the shelter of the rocky spur, Swift Pigeon looked at him with black, beady eyes and said nothing. The small papoose lying on its bed of dry grass stared at him in the same Indian silence. But for Eric there were only two things that counted—that he had found Mary Anne and that he needed sleep. He ate such food as the squaw could put before him, his eyes growing heavy even as he sat by the fire and tried to talk to Mary Anne. Then he curled up on a bed of willow boughs that the old Indian woman had got ready for him. The smell of the crushed leaves and the green twigs was sweet in his nostrils as he dropped his head upon his arm.

"If you want to wake me, blow the willow whistle," he said, and was instantly asleep.

All that night and well into the next day he slumbered. It was almost noon when he sat up, suddenly wide awake, rested, and as hungry as a wolf.

Swift Pigeon was making preparations for the homeward journey. She had gathered berries and roots. She had caught more fish and was showing Mary Anne how to wrap them with bark and willow leaves. Sancho was stuffing himself greedily with grass beside the creek. As Eric watched him graze, stepping from one stretch of green to another, the boy's heart sank. The stout little pony must

have strained a foreleg or a shoulder, which had stiffened with rest, for he moved forward with an awkward hobble. Yet lame as he was, he must give them what help he could on the long homeward trail.

They set out at sunset, since it would be safer to travel in the dark. Mary Anne and Swift Pigeon took turns in riding and carrying the baby. Eric trudged bravely ahead and Sancho limped behind. Slow progress they made, down the winding valley, over the ridges, and out on the great dark plain. Tonight there was not even a moon to light them from the clouded sky.

They traveled until midnight, stopped to rest a little, and then got up to plod on again. Sancho moved slower and slower; with all of Eric's urging he could scarcely stumble forward. Mary Anne uttered never a complaint; indeed, for the last five miles she had been too weary to speak at all. The patient baby whimpered softly but still did not cry. The old Indian woman muttered a little in her own tongue as she rocked the papoose in her arms.

Suddenly Swift Pigeon flung up her head to listen. They all heard the sound—horses' galloping feet coming from a great way off. Sancho stood still and lifted his own head to give a loud whinny.

"If it is white men coming, they will shout," Eric thought. He stood listening; the feet came nearer but no voice answered. Was it Indians? He did not have time to ponder long over what they should do. Two dark forms came blundering out of the darkness; then the dun-colored pony dropped his nose into Swift Pigeon's hand and stood nuzzling and nickering in soft delight.

Trailing behind him, attached to the hide rope that his captor had used for a bridle, was the long-legged horse which the Indian boy had ridden. It was not difficult to

369

guess just what had happened. The Sioux pony had loped along apparently quite obedient to the will of his new master, but actually biding his time. When the easy pace had lasted for hours, when the rider was quite satisfied and secure, when perhaps he had even dozed a little because of the drowsy, jogging motion—then was the little horse's moment. For an instant the Arickaree's hand was unsteady on the bridle; the dun pony's heels were up like a flash, and his head down between his knees. Over and over went the Indian rider, tumbling upon the grass. While the two horses galloped away into the dark, he was left to reflect upon the pleasure of walking fifty . . . sixty . . . a hundred miles home.

John Seabold and his companions had circled far over the prairie and had found no trace of Mary Anne. They passed a few scattered groups of Arickaree Indians driving horses southward, but these carried no captives, certainly no little girl. In the faint hope that Gray Eagle might have found his way to the cabin, the white men had ridden homeward. There they must get fresh horses if the hunt was still to go on.

They met Gray Eagle on the way, a haggard and desperate Gray Eagle who had searched for Mary Anne, as they had, without success. The chief had thought, also, that some of his braves might have caught up the little girl in the confusion and carried her home. John Seabold gave one glance at the Indian party and saw that Mary Anne was not with them. Thereafter he rode ahead with a stony face and said no word to the red men clattering behind him, not even when they all drew up together at the house beyond the creek.

Thus it came about that there was a knot of men, white

and red, and a group of weary horses and Indian ponies clustered before the door of the cabin just as the sun came up. It was exactly when the first rays touched the willows that they saw a little cavalcade come toiling across the green plain, a yellow-maned pony ridden by a boy, and a long, lean nag behind who carried a girl, a baby, and a bent squaw. When the sun rose higher it was to show also a tiny distant dot that was Sancho, limping homeward far in the rear.

The dun pony came splashing through the ford with the taller mount following him. The Arickaree horse had never seen white men; he hesitated, faltered, and shied as Swift Pigeon urged him up the bank. Mary Anne could wait for no delay; she slipped to the ground and went running up the path calling aloud, "Mother! Mother!"

Gray Eagle and John Seabold had not spoken to each other before, but now they turned, and each looked at the other steadily.

"How!" said Gray Eagle. It is so that an Indian greets a friend.

"How!" returned Mary Anne's father. It is so that a white man returns the greeting of an Indian whom he trusts. They both stood aside as Jane Seabold ran out of the cabin door to snatch her little daughter into hungrily welcoming arms.

THINKING ABOUT THE BOOK

Did you enjoy reading *The Willow Whistle*? A whole book is fun to read, for the characters so often become fast friends. Imagine the number of friends you can make in your library! What different kinds of book friends have you already met through your library card? When you think of Eric and Mary Anne and Gray Eagle, what will you especially remember about them?

KIDNAPPED?

What characters were introduced in this chapter?

How did Mary Anne's father try to help the Indians lead better lives?

Mary Anne was shy. Why do you think she was afraid to meet new people? What can we do that will help a shy person?

Eric made a willow whistle for Mary Anne. He met an Indian chief. What other things happened in this chapter?

There are some fine descriptions in this chapter. Choose one or two that seemed particularly interesting or vivid and read them aloud to the class. What picture-words or sentences made you choose them?

THE SEARCH PARTY

Tell in your own words what happened in this chapter.

Eric was not frightened when he saw that Gray Eagle was carrying Mary Anne away. How did Mrs. Seabold feel when Eric told her what happened?

When Mr. Seabold started out to find Mary Anne, why did he want to take Eric along? How did it happen that Eric was separated from the other people who were hunting for Mary Anne? How did he find the search party again?

When they reached the Sioux camp, the men could tell

that the Arickarees had come after the Sioux horses. How did they know there had not been a fight?

With the Indians

This part of the story took you back in time. It told about Mary Anne being carried away by Gray Eagle. How did Mary Anne feel when she knew that she was being taken away?

What new characters were introduced in this chapter?

The Indians were good to Mary Anne. What were some of the friendly things they did for her? Why was Mary Anne not homesick?

The Indian dance was new to Mary Anne. What was the purpose of the celebration? What interrupted the dance?

Eric Hears a Willow Whistle

While Eric was trying to find Mary Anne, he had an exciting adventure with a buffalo. Tell what happened.

In the great prairie it was hard to follow a trail. How did Eric finally know that Mary Anne was near?

Both Mary Anne and Eric showed bravery in this chapter. How could you tell that each one was brave?

Escape and Return

Eric and Mary Anne finally found each other. But they were still in danger. Why did Mary Anne tell Eric to speak in a whisper? Where did she get the willow whistle with which she signalled to Eric?

Swift Pigeon had taught Mary Anne to stay very still when danger was near. Why was this a good idea?

The Arickaree boy did not see Eric and Mary Anne. What was he looking for? Where had Eric met the

Arickaree before? How did the Arickaree catch Gray Eagle's pony?

Mary Anne was brave on the trip back to her home. How did she show her bravery? How did Eric get Gray Eagle's horse back again?

The story ends with a happy reunion. How did Eric and Mary Anne get back home?

When Eric and Mary Anne returned to the Seabold house, Gray Eagle and Mr. Seabold exchanged a greeting. What did they say? This shows us that they were true friends. Mr. Seabold did not blame Gray Eagle for what had happened to Mary Anne. Gray Eagle knew that Mr. Seabold trusted him.

It is through trust in one another that people learn to live together. Can you think of a time when you have learned to trust and believe in an acquaintance? Did this make you think of him as a friend?

The author called her book *The Willow Whistle*. Why do you think she chose that title? What other good titles can you make up for this story?

GLOSSARY

This glossary provides pronunciations and explanations of the more difficult words used in ACROSS THE BLUE BRIDGE. Each word is explained according to the way it is used in the text.

The glossary gives the part of speech for each word like this: *adj.* for adjective; *adv.* for adverb; *n.* for noun; *v.* for verb.

Understanding *accent marks* (′) (′) will help you pronounce words. The dark accent mark, as in mother (muth′ər), is placed *after* the part of the word that is said or accented most strongly. Sometimes a word will have a dark accent mark (′) and a lighter accent mark (′), as in grandmother (grand′muth′ər). The part of the word that is followed by (′) is accented most strongly, and the part of the word that is followed by (′) is given a little less accent.

A key to pronunciation is given below.

a	act, bat	ō	over, no	zh	vision, measure, sabotage
ā	able, cape	ô	order, ball		
â	air, dare	oi	oil, joy	ə	occurs only in the part of a word that is not accented, and it sounds like:
ä	art, calm, father	o͝o	book, put		
ch	chief, beach	o͞o	ooze, rule		
e	ebb, set	ou	out, loud		
ē	equal, bead, duty	sh	shoe, push	a	*in* alone
i	if, big	th	thin, path	e	*in* system
ī	ice, bite	th	that, other	i	*in* easily
ng	sing, song	u	up, love	o	*in* gallop
o	box, hot, wan	û(r)	urge, burn	u	*in* circus

A

abbot (ab′ət), *n.*   A man who governs a monastery.

absorbed (ab sôrbd′), *v.*   Soaked up.

accommodations (ə kom′ə dā′shənz), *n.*   Seat on a plane or train.

aerodrome (âr′ə drōm′), *n.*   An airport.

agate (ag′it), *n.*   A colored stone like a child's marble.

agile (aj′əl), *adj.*   Able to move quickly and easily.

alfalfa (al fal′fə), *n.*   A plant used for food for cattle and horses.

allies (al′īz), *n.*   Countries joined by treaty during a war.

allude (ə lo͞od′), *v.*   To refer to casually; to mention.

altimeter (al tim′ə tər), *n.*   An instrument for measuring altitude.

amble (am′bəl), *v.*   To move in a gentle, easy gait.

anxiety (ang zī′ə tē), *n.*   Uneasiness of mind; fearful unrest; worry.

apt (apt), *adj.* Likely.

arrogant (ar′ə gənt), *adj.* Thinking too highly of oneself; conceited.

assist (ə sist′), *v.* To help someone.

assure (ə shŏŏr′), *v.* To make certain.

athwart (ə thwôrt′), *adv.* Crosswise; from side to side.

authority (ə thôr′ə tē), *n.* A person in power, as in the government.

awed (ôd), *adj.* Having a feeling of respect and wonder.

B

balked (bôkd), *v.* Stopped; refused to go.

balusters (bal′ə stərs), *n.* Posts that support stair railings.

barnacle (bär′nə kəl), *n.* A small shellfish that fastens itself on the bottom of boats.

beaker (bē′kər), *n.* A large drinking vessel with a wide mouth.

bijou (bē′zhŏŏ), *adj.* Something small and special.

bower (bou′ər), *n.* Bedroom.

brayed (brād), *v.* Made a loud noise like a donkey.

bulkheads (bulk′hedz′), *n.* The upright partitions separating sections in a ship.

C

calculation (kal′kyə lā′shən), *n.* The act of figuring out something very carefully by mathematics.

camouflage (kam′ə fläzh′), *n.* A disguise to make something hard to see.

capered (kā′pərd), *v.* Jumped or leaped about.

caravan (kar′ə van′), *n.* Many merchants traveling together.

cavalcade (kav′əl kād′), *n.* A procession of people on horseback.

ceremonies (ser′ə mō′nēz), *n.* Formal occasions which follow certain set rules or patterns.

chafed (chāft), *v.* Rubbed the skin until it was sore.

chamois (sham′ē), *n.* A goatlike antelope or deer.

chasm (kaz′əm), *n.* A deep opening in the earth.

chlorine (klōr′ēn), *n.* A poisonous gas.

climax (klī′maks), *n.* The most important or exciting time of a story or happening.

cloven (klō′vən), *adj.* Cut.

collide (kə līd′), *v.* To crash into something with force.

compliment (kom′plə mənt), *v.* To praise.

composedly (kəm pō′zid lē), *adv.* Calmly; without excitement.

comrade (kom′rad), *n.* A friend or companion.

concealed (kən sēld), *adj.* Hidden.

confined (kən fīnd′), *v.* Held within a certain area.

congratulate (kən grach′ə lāt′), *v.* To praise or to express pleasure over someone's happiness or good fortune.

consulted (kən sult′əd), *v.* Asked advice or opinion of another.

contact (kon′takt), *n.* Getting in touch with someone or something.

contagious (kən tā′jəs), *adj.* Easily spread, as a disease.

contemptuous (kən temp′chŏŏ əs), *adj.* Scornful.

contend (kən tend′), *v.* To put up with something disagreeable.

copse (kops), *n.* A thick growth of small trees.

corporation (kôr′pə rā′shən), *n.* A group of persons organized to carry on a business.

cottonwood (kot′ən wŏŏd′), *n.* A tree with light-colored bark, and seeds with tufts of hair looking like cotton.

countenance (koun′tə nəns), *n.* The face.

courteous (kûr′ti əs), *adj.* Polite.

covey (kuv′ē), *n.* A small flock of quail.

cowering (kou′ər ing), *v.* Crouching or bending down as if in fear.

cowl (koul), *n.* A monk's hood which is attached to his gown.

D

defiant (di fī′ənt), *adj.* Not willing to obey orders.

deft (deft), *adj.* Quick and neat.

demonstration (dem′ən strā′shən), *n.* The act of showing how something works.

desperately (des′pər it lē), *adv.* Almost without hope.

destination (des′tə nā′shən), *n.* The end of a journey.

devoutly (di vout′lē), *adv.* Sincerely; earnestly.

diadem (dī′ə dem′), *n.* A crown.

dinghy (ding′gē), *n.* A small, light rowboat.

disgrace (dis grās′), *n.* Shame; loss of respect or honor.

dislodge (dis loj′), *v.* To loosen or force out.

distinction (dis tingk′shən), *n.* Having some special recognition.

douse (dous), *v.* To cover with water.

drone (drōn), *n.* A low, monotonous, humming sound.

duly (dyōō′lē), *adv.* Properly; in a fit manner.

E

ecstasy (ek′stə sē), *n.*   Great happiness.
egotistic (ē′gə tis′tic), *adj.*   Conceited; boastful.
embittered (em bit′ərd), *adj.*   Having a bitter feeling.
enthusiastic (en thoō′zi as′tik), *adj.*   Eager.
entice (en tīs′), *v.*   To tempt someone to do something.
errant (er′ənt), *adj.*   Wandering around looking for adventure.
exceeds (ik sēdz′), *v.*   Goes beyond the limit.
exclusive (ik skloō′siv), *adj.*   Having sole ownership of something.
excruciatingly (ik skroō′shi ā′ting lē), *adv.*   Painfully.
excursions (ik skûr′zhəns), *n.*   Pleasure trips.
experimenting (ik sper′ə ment′ing), *v.*   Testing; trying to prove.
exultantly (ig zul′tənt lē), *adv.*   Triumphantly.

F

fascinating (fas′ə nā′ting), *adj.*   Very attractive.
fen (fen), *n.*   Marsh.
fiction (fik′shən), *n.*   Stories about imaginary people or happenings.
flagstaff (flag′staf′), *n.*   A pole on which a flag is displayed.
floundering (floun′dər ing), *v.*   Struggling in a clumsy way.
forbade (fer bad′), *v.*   Told someone not to do something.
forbore (fôr bōr′), *v.*   Did without; held back from.
frantic (fran′tik), *adj.*   Very excited.
fraying (frā′ing), *v.*   Becoming worn at the edges.
friar (frī′ər), *n.*   A member of a religious order.
fuselage (fyoō′zə lij), *n.*   The part of an airplane where passengers
   sit; the wings and tail are attached to it.

G

galvanized (gal′və nīzd′), *adj.*   Coated with zinc.
gauge (gāj), *n.*   An instrument for measuring something.
gingerly (jin′jər lē), *adv.*   Using special care and caution.
gingham (ging′əm), *n.*   A cotton material in plain colors, checks, or
   plaids.
girth (gûrth), *n.*   A band placed around a horse's body on which to
   fasten a blanket.
glens (glens), *n.*   Hidden valleys.
gory (gōr′ē), *adj.*   Bloody.

gravely (grāv′lē), *adv.*   Seriously; importantly.
grimly (grim′lē), *adv.*   Sternly.

H

hackamore (hak′ə mōr′), *n.*   A coil of rope that goes through a horse's mouth and around his neck, used to break a horse.
haggard (hag′ərd), *adj.*   Worried or pained looking.
half-heartedly (haf′här′tid lē), *adv.*   Without much desire.
handicap (han′di kap′), *n.*   Something that makes progress difficult.
harrowed (har′ōd), *v.*   Broke the soil and smoothed it over, as in farming.
hindrance (hin′drəns), *n.*   That which keeps one from doing something.
horsepower (hôrs′pou′ər), *n.*   Unit for measuring power.
humiliated (hyo͞o mil′i ā′tid), *adj.*   Embarrassed.
hydrogen (hī′drə jən), *n.*   A colorless, tasteless, odorless gas that is the lightest substance known.
hysterical (his ter′ə kəl), *adj.*   Wildly excited.

I

impact (im′pakt), *n.*   A striking together with great force.
imperiously (im pir′i əs lē), *adv.*   Urgently; commandingly.
impertinence (im pûr′tə nəns), *n.*   Rudeness.
impression (im presh′ən), *n.*   A feeling that something might be so.
impromptu (im promp′to͞o), *adj.*   Something done in a hurry and without preparations.
incantation (in′kan tā′shən), *n.*   A magic charm or spell.
indulge (in dulj′), *v.*   To give in to someone's desires.
innermost (in′ər mōst′), *adj.*   Deep inside.
insatiable (in sā′shə bəl), *adj.*   Not able to be satisfied.
inscribed (in skrībd′), *adj.*   Written upon, as an engraving, in order to last a long time.
intense (in tens′), *adj.*   Very extreme, as intense cold.
intently (in tent′lē), *adv.*   With close attention.
interior (in tir′i ər), *n.*   The inside of anything.
interpreter (in tûr′pri tər), *n.*   One who repeats in a familiar language what has been said in a foreign language.
interval (in′tər vəl), *n.*   The time between certain happenings.

intoxicated (in tox′sə kā′tid), *adj.* Overcome or drunk with excitement or happiness.
invade (in vād′), *v.* To attack with armed forces.

J

jerkins (jûr′kinz), *n.* Jackets or short coats.
jodhpurs (jod′pərz), *n.* Riding breeches reaching to the ankle.
jovial (jō′vi əl), *adj.* Happy; merry.

K

keel (kēl), *n.* The bottom of a boat, along the center.
keelboat (kēl′bōt′), *n.* A freight boat or barge.
knickers (nik′ərz), *n.* Short pants that are gathered at the knee.

L

lance (lans), *n.* A long-handled weapon with a sharp steel head.
lariat (lar′i ət), *n.* A rope with a slipknot, used to catch horses.
lee (lē), *n.* Shelter; the side or part that is away from the wind.
lurch (lûrch), *v.* To sway suddenly to one side.
luxurious (lug zho͝or′i əs), *adj.* Very expensive and elegant.

M

marathon (mar′ə thon′), *n.* A long-lasting contest.
mastered (mas′tərd), *v.* Learned to do something well.
menacing (men′is ing), *n.* Threatening to cause harm.
mess hall (mes′hôl′), *n.* A place where military groups eat together.
mettle (met′əl), *n.* Courage.
microbe (mī′krōb), *n.* A plant or animal that can only be seen through a microscope.
milling (mil′ing), *v.* A group of people or animals moving about in a confused or disorderly manner.
miracles (mir′ə kəlz), *n.* Unexplained, wonderful happenings.
mischievous (mis′chə vəs), *adj.* Full of mischief.
molest (mə lest′), *v.* To annoy or harm someone.
monastery (mon′ə ster′ē), *n.* A building in which monks live.
monotonously (mə not′ə nəs lē), *adv.* Continually; repeatedly, in the same way.
murky (mûr′kē), *adj.* Thick with mist or haze.

N

necromancer (nek′rə man′sər), *n.* A magician.
nectar (nek′tər), *n.*   Any delicious drink.
nestlings (nest′lings), *n.* Baby birds unable to leave the nest.
nourishing (nûr′ish ing), *adj.* Health and energy giving.

O

obstinate (ob′stə nit), *adj.* Stubborn.
offensive (ə fen′siv), *n.* An attack.
outlandish (out lan′dish), *adj.* Strange or different.

P

parallel (par′ə lel′), *adj.* Lying or moving in the same direction.
parchment (pärch′mənt), *n.* Paper, made from skin of sheep or
    goats, that can be written on.
pedigree (ped′ə grē′), *n.* The ancestry of a person or animal.
penetrating (pen′ə trä ting), *adj.* Entering deeply; piercing.
permanent (pûr′mə nənt), *adj.* Lasting a very long time.
peso (pā′sō), *n.* A Spanish or Mexican dollar.
petrified (pet′rə fīd), *adj.* Turned to stone.
picturesque (pik′chə resk′), *adj.* Almost like a picture; quaint.
piebald (pī′bôld′), *adj.* Black and white; mottled.
plaque (plak), *n.* A thin, flat piece of metal or clay with words or
    pictures on it.
plunder (plun′dər), *v.* To rob or steal.
portmanteau (pōrt man′tō), *n.* A carrying case for clothing, as a
    suitcase.
presumed (pri zo͞omd′), *v.* Thought something was true without
    proof.
privilege (priv′ə lij), *n.* The right to do something very special.
prosper (pros′pər), *v.* To be successful.
provender (prov′ən dər), *n.* Dry food for animals, such as hay.
pursuit (pər so͞ot′), *n.* The act of chasing.

Q

quiver (kwiv′ər), *n.* A case used for carrying arrows.

R

ransom (ran′səm), *n.* Money paid in order to set free someone who
  has been captured.

rapture (rap′chər), *n.* A very joyous feeling.

ravine (rə vēn′), *n.* A gorge or gully.

readily (red′ə lē), *adv.* Quickly or easily.

reassuring (rē′ə shŏŏr′ing), *adj.* Comforting; giving confidence.

rebellion (ri bel′yən), *n.* Uprising against the law.

recollected (rek′ə lek′tid), *v.* Remembered.

reconnaissance (ri kon′ə səns), *adj.* Search for military information
  on the ground.

reflect (ri flekt′), *v.* To think seriously.

regulations (reg′yə lā′shəns), *n.* Rules, as in the army.

reminiscently (rem′ə nis′ənt lē), *adv.* Recalling things that happened
  in the past.

remote (ri mōt′), *adj.* To be far off in place or time.

resinous (rez′ ə nəs), *adj.* Pertaining to resin, the gum or sap from
  pine trees.

resounding (ri zoun′ding), *adj.* Loud and echoing in sound.

restless (rest′lis), *adj.* Uneasy; not at rest; not still.

reveille (rev′ə lē), *n.* A bugle call sounded at daybreak to rouse
  soldiers.

revelation (rev′ə lā′shən), *n.* Something revealed or brought into
  the open.

routine (rōō tēn′), *n.* Activities done regularly.

rowlocks (rō′loks′), *n.* The places on a rowboat where the oars are
  fastened.

S

sacrifice (sak′rə fīs′), *n.* An unselfish act of giving up something.

sagebrush (sāj′brush′), *n.* A low plant with bitter juice found in
  western United States.

score (skōr), *n.* Twenty.

scrawny (skrô′nē), *adj.* Painfully thin.

sculled (skuld), *v.* Rowed a boat.

seclusion (si klōō′zhən), *n.* The act of hiding away because of a
  wish to be alone.

sedately (si dāt′lē), *adv.* Quietly, soberly.

serpentine (sûr'pən tēn'), *adj.* Winding, like a snake.

shampooed (sham pōōd'), *v.* Washed the hair and scalp.

shroud (shroud), *n.* A rope that goes from the masthead of a boat to the side to support the mast.

shuttle (shut'əl), *n.* An instrument used to carry the thread back and forth on the loom when weaving.

shy (shī), *adj.* Quiet and a little fearful or bashful of public notice.

situation (sich'ōō ā'shən), *n.* A place or a location.

sixpence (siks'pəns), *n.* An English coin.

skirted (skûrt'tid), *v.* Went around the edge of.

specifications (spes'ə fə kā'shəns), *n.* The description of what is to be done in building something.

speedometer (spē dom'ə tər), *n.* An instrument which measures speed and distance.

spires (spīrs), *n.* Steeples on a church.

stability (stə bil'ə tē), *n.* Steadiness or firmness.

staff (staf), *n.* A long stick.

stature (stach'ər), *n.* Height.

stoat (stōt), *n.* The ermine, when it has its brown summer coat.

stowaway (stō'ə wā'), *n.* A person hiding in a ship in order to obtain free passage.

strand (strand), *n.* Shore line.

strife (strīf), *n.* A fight or quarrel.

submitted (səb mi'tid), *v.* Surrendered.

substitute (sub'stə tyōōt'), *n.* Something which takes the place of another.

sullenly (sul'ən lē), *adv.* Gloomily.

surging (sûr'jing), *v.* Rushing onward.

suspended (sə spen'did), *v.* Hung above.

suspiciously (sə spish'əs lē), *adv.* Acting as if something were wrong.

T

tailor-wise (tā'lər wīs'), *adj.* Sitting cross-legged, as a tailor.

taunts (tônts), *v.* Teases or ridicules.

taut (tôt), *adj.* Tightly drawn; firm.

tedious (tēd'di əs), *adj.* Boring; tiresome.

tempest (tem'pist), *n.* A violent wind.

tense (tens), *adj.* Nervous and strained.

thoroughly (thûr'ō lē), *adv.* Completely.

thoughtful (thôt′fəl), *adj.* Having care for another's feelings.

timid (tim′id), *adj.* Rather fearful; not adventuresome.

tormenting (tôr ment′ing), *v.* Causing someone to suffer.

tourist (tŏor′ist), *n.* One who travels for pleasure.

traits (trāts), *n.* Characteristics.

translated (trans lā′tid), *v.* Repeated in a familiar language what has been said in a foreign language.

transmit (trans mit′), *v.* To pass from one place or person to another.

transparent (trans pâr′ənt), *adj.* Very clear; able to be seen through.

tremendous (tri men′dəs), *adj.* Very large or powerful.

U

unbounded (un boun′did), *adj.* Unlimited or uncontrolled.

unflinching (un flin′ching), *adj.* Not giving up or backing away.

unfortunately (un fôr′chə nit lē), *adv.* Unluckily.

unison (yōo′nə sən), *n.* Acting as one person; harmony.

unruly (un rōo′lē), *adj.* Not able to be controlled.

unwitting (un wit′ing), *adj.* Not knowing.

V

vanished (van′isht), *v.* Disappeared from sight.

vibrating (vī′brā ting), *v.* Shaking back and forth.

visible (viz′ə bəl), *adj.* Able to be seen.

vivid (viv′id), *adj.* Something very clear.

W

weir (wir), *n.* A dam in a river.

weird (wird), *adj.* Ghostly and unnatural.

wields (wēlds), *v.* Uses an instrument skillfully.

windbreaker (wind′brā′kər), *n.* A short jacket made of leather.

wistfully (wist′fəl lē), *adv.* Longingly.

Y

yeomen (yō′mən), *n.* English farmers who owned their own land.

384